Spiral to Infinity Steve Allen

"Fractal images are often made up of small images-within-images, constantly repeating and going smaller and smaller."– **Steve Allen**

D1365055

Investigations
IN NUMBER, DATA, AND SPACE®

Power Polygons™ is a trademark of ETA/Cuisenaire®.

Use of the trademark or company name implies no relationship, sponsorship, endorsement, sale, or promotion on the part of Pearson Education, Inc., or its affiliates.

Glenview, Illinois • Boston, Massachusetts
Chandler, Arizona • Upper Saddle River, New Jersey

The Investigations curriculum was developed by TERC, Cambridge, MA.

This material is based on work supported by the National Science Foundation ("NSF") under Grant No. ESI-0095450. Any opinions, findings, and conclusions or recommendations expressed in this material are those of the author(s) and do not necessarily reflect the views of the National Science Foundation.

ISBN-13: 978-0-328-60005-2

ISBN-10: 0-328-60005-9

1 2 3 4 5 6 7 8 9 10 V003 14 13 12 11 10

T E R C

Co-Principal Investigators

Susan Jo Russell

Karen Economopoulos

Authors

Lucy Wittenberg
Director Grades 3–5

Karen Economopoulos
Director Grades K–2

Virginia Bastable
(SummerMath for Teachers,
Mt. Holyoke College)

Katie Hickey Bloomfield

Keith Cochran

Darrell Earnest

Arusha Hollister

Nancy Horowitz

Erin Leidl

Megan Murray

Young Oh

Beth W. Perry

Susan Jo Russell

Deborah Schifter
(Education
Development Center)

Kathy Sillman

Administrative Staff

Amy Taber
Project Manager

Beth Bergeron

Lorraine Brooks

Emi Fujiwara

Contributing Authors

Denise Baumann

Jennifer DiBrienza

Hollee Freeman

Paula Hooper

Jan Mokros

Stephen Monk
(University of Washington)

Mary Beth O'Connor

Judy Storeygard

Cornelia Tierney

Elizabeth Van Cleef

Carol Wright

Technology

Jim Hammerman

Classroom Field Work

Amy Appell

Rachel E. Davis

Traci Higgins

Julia Thompson

Note: Unless otherwise noted, all contributors listed above were staff of the Education Research Collaborative at TERC during their work on the curriculum. Other affiliations during the time of development are listed.

Collaborating Teachers

This group of dedicated teachers carried out extensive field testing in their classrooms, met regularly to discuss issues of teaching and learning mathematics, provided feedback to staff, welcomed staff into their classrooms to document students' work, and contributed both suggestions and written material that has been incorporated into the curriculum.

Bethany Altchek

Linda Amaral

Kimberly Beauregard

Barbara Bernard

Nancy Buell

Rose Christiansen

Chris Colbath-Hess

Lisette Colon

Kim Cook

Frances Cooper

Kathleen Drew

Rebeka Eston Salemi

Thomas Fisher

Michael Flynn

Holly Ghazey

Susan Gillis

Danielle Harrington

Elaine Herzog

Francine Hiller

Kirsten Lee Howard

Liliana Klass

Leslie Kramer

Melissa Lee Andrichak

Kelley Lee Sadowski

Jennifer Levitan

Mary Lou LoVecchio

Kristen McEnaney

Maura McGrail

Kathe Millett

Florence Molyneaux

Amy Monkiewicz

Elizabeth Monopoli

Carol Murray

Robyn Musser

Christine Norrman

Deborah O'Brien

Timothy O'Connor

Anne Marie O'Reilly

Mark Paige

Margaret Riddle

Karen Schweitzer

Elisabeth Seyferth

Susan Smith

Debra Sorvillo

Shoshanah Starr

Janice Szymaszek

Karen Tobin

JoAnn Trauschke

Ana Vaisenstein

Yvonne Watson

Michelle Woods

Mary Wright

Advisors

Deborah Lowenberg Ball,
University of Michigan

Hyman Bass, Professor of Mathematics and Mathematics Education
University of Michigan

Mary Canner, Principal, Natick Public Schools

Thomas Carpenter, Professor of Curriculum and Instruction,
University of Wisconsin-Madison

Janis Freckmann, Elementary Mathematics Coordinator,
Milwaukee Public Schools

Lynne Godfrey, Mathematics Coach,
Cambridge Public Schools

Ginger Hanlon, Instructional Specialist in Mathematics,
New York City Public Schools

DeAnn Huinker, Director, Center for Mathematics and
Science Education Research, University of Wisconsin-Milwaukee

James Kaput, Professor of Mathematics, University of
Massachusetts-Dartmouth

Kate Kline, Associate Professor, Department of Mathematics
and Statistics, Western Michigan University

Jim Lewis, Professor of Mathematics,
University of Nebraska-Lincoln

William McCallum, Professor of Mathematics,
University of Arizona

Harriet Pollatsek, Professor of Mathematics,
Mount Holyoke College

Debra Shein-Gerson, Elementary Mathematics Specialist,
Weston Public Schools

Gary Shevell, Assistant Principal,
New York City Public Schools

Liz Sweeney, Elementary Math Department,
Boston Public Schools

Lucy West, Consultant, Metamorphosis:
Teaching Learning Communities, Inc.

This revision of the curriculum was built on the work of the many authors who contributed to the first edition (published between 1994 and 1998). We acknowledge the critical contributions of these authors in developing the content and pedagogy of *Investigations*:

Authors

Joan Akers

Michael T. Battista

Douglas H. Clements

Karen Economopoulos

Marlene Kliman

Jan Mokros

Megan Murray

Ricardo Nemirovsky

Andee Rubin

Susan Jo Russell

Cornelia Tierney

Contributing Authors

Mary Berle-Carman

Rebecca B. Corwin

Rebeka Eston

Claryce Evans

Anne Goodrow

Cliff Konold

Chris Mainhart

Sue McMillen

Jerrie Moffet

Tracy Noble

Kim O'Neil

Mark Ogonowski

Julie Sarama

Amy Shulman Weinberg

Margie Singer

Virginia Woolley

Tracey Wright

Contents

UNIT 4

What Would You Rather Be?

Investigations

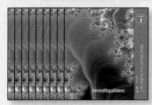

Overview of Program Components

FOR TEACHERS

The **Curriculum Units** are the teaching guides. (See far right.)

Implementing Investigations in Grade 1 offers suggestions for implementing the curriculum. It also contains a comprehensive index.

The **Differentiation and Intervention Guide** offers additional activities for each Investigation to support the range of learners.

Investigations for the Interactive Whiteboard provides whole-class instructional support to enhance each session.

The **Resource Masters and Transparencies CD** contains all reproducible materials that support instruction. The **Shapes CD** provides an environment in which students investigate a variety of geometric ideas.

FOR STUDENTS

The **Student Activity Book** contains the consumable student pages (Recording Sheets, Homework, Practice, and so on).

The **Student Math Handbook** contains Math Words and Ideas pages and Games directions.

The *Investigations* Curriculum

Investigations in Number, Data, and Space® is a K–5 mathematics curriculum designed to engage students in making sense of mathematical ideas. Six major goals guided the development of the *Investigations in Number, Data, and Space*® curriculum. The curriculum is designed to:

- Support students to make sense of mathematics and learn that they can be mathematical thinkers

- Focus on computational fluency with whole numbers as a major goal of the elementary grades

- Provide substantive work in important areas of mathematics—rational numbers, geometry, measurement, data, and early algebra—and connections among them

- Emphasize reasoning about mathematical ideas

- Communicate mathematics content and pedagogy to teachers

- Engage the range of learners in understanding mathematics

Underlying these goals are three guiding principles that are touchstones for the *Investigations* team as we approach both students and teachers as agents of their own learning:

1. *Students have mathematical ideas.* Students come to school with ideas about numbers, shapes, measurements, patterns, and data. If given the opportunity to learn in an environment that stresses making sense of mathematics, students build on the ideas they already have and learn about new mathematics they have never encountered. Students learn that they are capable of having mathematical ideas, applying what they know to new situations, and thinking and reasoning about unfamiliar problems.

2. *Teachers are engaged in ongoing learning* about mathematics content, pedagogy, and student learning. The curriculum provides material for professional development, to be used by teachers individually or in groups, that supports teachers' continued learning as they use the curriculum over several years. The *Investigations* curriculum materials are designed as much to be a dialogue with teachers as to be a core of content for students.

3. *Teachers collaborate with the students and curriculum materials* to create the curriculum as enacted in the classroom. The only way for a good curriculum to be used well is for teachers to be active participants in implementing it. Teachers use the curriculum to maintain a clear, focused, and coherent agenda for mathematics teaching. At the same time, they observe and listen carefully to students, try to understand how they are thinking, and make teaching decisions based on these observations.

Investigations is based on experience from research and practice, including field testing that involved documentation of thousands of hours in classrooms, observations of students, input from teachers, and analysis of student work. As a result, the curriculum addresses the learning needs of real students in a wide range of classrooms and communities. The investigations are carefully designed to invite all students into mathematics—girls and boys; members of diverse cultural, ethnic, and language groups; and students with a wide variety of strengths, needs, and interests.

Based on this extensive classroom testing, the curriculum takes seriously the time students need to develop a strong conceptual foundation and skills based on that foundation. Each curriculum unit focuses on an area of content in depth, providing time for students to develop and practice ideas across a variety of activities and contexts that build on each other. Daily guidelines for time spent on class sessions, Classroom Routines (K–3), and Ten-Minute Math (3–5) reflect the commitment to devoting adequate time to mathematics in each school day.

About This Curriculum Unit

This **Curriculum Unit** is one of nine teaching guides in Grade 1. The fourth unit in Grade 1 is *What Would You Rather Be?*.

- The **Introduction and Overview** section organizes and presents the instructional materials, provides background information, and highlights important features specific to this unit.

- Each Curriculum Unit contains several **Investigations.** Each Investigation focuses on a set of related mathematical ideas.

- Investigations are divided into one-hour **Sessions,** or lessons.

- Sessions have a combination of these parts: **Activity, Discussion, Math Workshop, Assessment Activity,** and **Session Follow-Up.**

- Each session also has one or more **Classroom Routines** that are done outside of math time.

- At the back of the book is a collection of **Teacher Notes** and **Dialogue Boxes** that provide professional development related to the unit.

- Also included at the back of the book are the **Student Math Handbook** pages for this unit.

- The **Index** provides a way to look up important words or terms.

Overview

O F   T H I S   U N I T

Investigation	Session	Day	
INVESTIGATION 1 **Sorting** Students describe and sort collections of objects according to specific attributes. They make representations that show how the objects are sorted. Students are introduced to *Quick Survey,* an activity that provides students with several opportunities throughout this unit to collect, record, and discuss data and to see a variety of standard data representations.	**1.1** Sorting Shapes	1	
	1.2 Sorting Buttons	2	
	1.3 Guess My Rule	3	
	1.4 Guess My Rule with People	4	
INVESTIGATION 2 **Collecting and Representing Data** Students focus on collecting, recording, and representing data as they develop their own survey questions and carry out a data collection project. Representing data in different ways, describing and comparing the data represented, and then interpreting the results of a survey is the focus of their work. Students complete an assessment in the last session of this investigation.	**2.1** What Would You Rather Be?	5	
	2.2 "Eagle or Whale?" Representations	6	
	2.3 Surveys	7	
	2.4 Representing Survey Data	8	
	2.5 Assessment: "Deep Sea or Outer Space?" Representations	9	
INVESTIGATION 3 **Comparing Age Data** Students use data about their ages and those of their siblings as they focus on collecting and representing numerical data. They compare their age data with the data from another first-grade class. Students complete an End-of-Unit Assessment that assesses the benchmarks associated with this unit.	**3.1** How Old Are We?	10	
	3.2 Ages of Another Class	11	
	3.3 Comparing Age Data	12	
	3.4 End-of-Unit Assessment	13	

Each *Investigations* session has some combination of these five parts: **Activity, Discussion, Math Workshop, Assessment Activity,** and **Session Follow-Up.** These session parts are indicated in the chart below. Each session also has one **Classroom Routine** that is done outside of math time.

 (W) Interactive Whiteboard

Activity	Discussion	Math Workshop	Assessment Activity	Session Follow-Up
(W) ● ●	(W)			●
● (W)	●			●
(W)	●	●		●
●	(W)	●		●
(W) ● ●	(W)			●
● ●	(W)			●
(W) (W) ●				●
● ●	●			●
	●		●	●
(W) ● ●				●
(W) ●	●			●
● ● ●				●
●			●	●

Classroom Routines

Morning Meeting	Quick Images	Start With/Get To
		(W)
		(W)
(W)		
	(W)	
		(W)
(W)		
		(W)
	(W)	
		(W)
		(W)
	(W)	
		(W)
	(W)	

Mathematics

IN THIS UNIT

What Would You Rather Be? is the fourth of nine units in the Grade 1 sequence. It is the Grade 1 unit in the Data Analysis and Probability strand of the *Investigations* curriculum. These units develop ideas about collecting, representing, describing, and interpreting data in Grades K–5 and about predicting likelihood of events in Grades 4–5.

LOOKING BACK In Kindergarten, students collected and represented data by counting. They counted and represented the number of people in the classroom and the number of eyes in the classroom. They sorted and counted their favorite lunch foods and carried out simple surveys using "Do You Like?" questions. Their work focused on counting, sorting into two groups, and collecting and representing data to answer questions about their class.

This unit focuses on 4 Mathematical Emphases:

1 Data Analysis Sorting and classifying

Math Focus Points

◆ Describing attributes of objects

◆ Using attributes to sort a set of objects

◆ Looking carefully at a group of objects to determine how they have been sorted

Sorting and classifying are processes that underlie many areas of mathematics, including work with data. In Grade 1, students' work focuses on sorting groups of related objects, such as buttons, and describing what distinguishes one group from another. Classifying by particular attributes is an important new area for young students. This early work in classification provides experience in considering only certain attributes of an object while ignoring others: it does not matter whether a button is round, square, large, or small in order to place it in the "shiny" group. In order to

decide whether an object belongs in a certain group, students have to define the criteria by which they are sorting. Does this button go in the "shiny" group? Does this shape fit in the "pointy corners" group?

Students find different ways of sorting objects.

Sorting a variety of sets lays the foundation for later work in classifying shapes and numbers and in working with categorical data. A triangle is not a triangle because "it kind of looks like a triangle," but because it can be defined as having a particular combination of attributes that only triangles have. A set of responses to the question "What is your favorite book?" can be sorted by different attributes (e.g., fiction or nonfiction, picture book or chapter book) in order to provide different views of the data.

2 Data Analysis Representing data

Math Focus Points

◆ Making a representation to communicate the results of a survey

◆ Making sense of data representations, including pictures, bar graphs, tallies, and Venn diagrams

◆ Comparing what different representations communicate about a set of data

◆ Using equations to show how the sum of the responses in each category equals the total responses collected

◆ Organizing data in numerical order

Data representation is both a tool for organizing and understanding data for oneself, and a way to communicate the results of data collection and analysis to others. The emphasis in this unit is on first graders' creating their own representations in order to organize their data and provide an image that helps them describe what the data show. Students are also introduced to several standard forms of representation, including picture graphs, tallies, charts, bar graphs, and Venn diagrams.

When developing their own representations of the data, students focus on what their data can tell them and how to make that clear for themselves and others. Through discussing and comparing representations, students consider what features of a representation help communicate a clear description of the data.

3 Data Analysis **Describing data**

Math Focus Points

◆ Describing and comparing the number of pieces of data in each category or at each value and interpreting what the data tell you about the group

◆ Understanding that the sum of the pieces of data in all the categories equals the number of people surveyed

◆ Using data to compare how two groups are similar or different

The key question in describing data in this unit is this: What do these data tell us about our class [the class next door, our siblings]? In the context of this overall question, first graders' descriptions focus on two characteristics of the data:

• What is the number of pieces of data in each category or at each value? (How many people wanted to be eagles? How many people are 7 years old?)

• Which category has more data? (Did more people want to be eagles or whales?)

In addition, students consider the sum of the data in all categories and the relationship of the sum to the total number of students in the class: if there are 24 students in the class, and everyone was present on the day we took the survey, then we should have 24 pieces of data in all the categories together.

In Investigation 2, students focus on categorical data—data that have values that can be classified into categories but do not have a quantitative value. The data collected for a question such as "Would you rather be an eagle or a whale?" falls into several categories: *whale, eagle,* and perhaps *both* or *neither.* The number of pieces of data in each category can be counted and compared with other categories.

> 14 children want to be whales,
> 9 want to be eagles, and 1 doesn't
> want to be either.

In Investigation 3, students work with numerical data as they collect data on their own ages and the ages of their siblings. In Grade 1, students describe numerical data in the same way they describe categorical data: they count and compare the number of pieces of data at each value.

> 14 children are 7 years old, and
> 10 children are 6 years old.

However, numerical data such as the ages of siblings can also be ordered so that students can see on a graph the "shape of the data"—how the data are concentrated or spread out. First graders may begin to think a bit about

"clumps" of data that they see on their age chart. For example, students in the **Dialogue Box:** Us and Our Siblings, page 143, wonder whether there are more siblings younger than they are or older than they are as they look at the representation of ages.

4 Data Analysis Designing and carrying out a data investigation

Math Focus Points

◆ Interpreting results of a data investigation

◆ Choosing a survey question

◆ Making a plan for gathering data

◆ Collecting and keeping track of survey data

Data are collected in a context and for a purpose. Data are used to answer a question, to investigate an issue, or to provide information about something in the world that is of interest. In Investigation 2, students carry out their own data investigation. They develop a question, collect the data, represent the data, and describe and interpret the data. This may, in turn, bring up more questions. After data have been collected, they are represented, examined, and analyzed to find out what information the data provide about the original questions. In Grade 1, students are also just beginning to consider aspects of how their data collection process affects what they can learn from their data. For example, an important issue for first graders who are surveying their classmates is how to keep track of which students they have asked. How do they know that they are surveying each person in the class and not asking anyone more than once? Already these students are considering how to make sure that their data are reliable: Do the data represent one response from each student? First graders also consider other issues that affect the outcome of their investigation, including how to treat responses that do not fit into their categories.

Classroom Routines focus on

◆ Developing strategies for counting accurately

◆ Using the calendar as a tool for keeping track of time

◆ Developing vocabulary to talk about time (*morning, noon, midday, afternoon,* etc.) and sequence (*first, next, last, before, after,* etc.)

◆ Collecting and recording data

◆ Making sense of a variety of representations of data

◆ Connecting written numbers and number names

◆ Using the number line as a tool for counting

◆ Using the 100 chart as a tool for counting

◆ Practicing the forward and backward counting sequences with numbers up to 60

◆ Developing and analyzing visual images for quantities

◆ Identifying and naming coins

LOOKING FORWARD

In Grade 2, students continue working with categorical data, but a primary focus is on collecting, representing, and describing numerical data. Through investigating such questions as "How many pockets do you have?" they think through the meaning of two ways that numbers are used in describing the data: some numbers indicate the value of a piece of data (I have 8 pockets); other numbers indicate how often a particular data value occurs (7 *children* have 8 pockets). Students continue to develop their own representations and also use bar graphs, Venn diagrams, line plots, and tallies. In Grade 3, students begin their work on seeing a data set as a whole, an idea that they continue to work on through the elementary years as they develop tools for characterizing and summarizing a set of data and using these summaries to compare groups.

Assessment

ONGOING ASSESSMENT: Observing Students at Work

The following sessions provide **Ongoing Assessment: Observing Students at Work** opportunities:

- **Session 1.1, pp. 24, 25, and 27**
- **Session 1.2, pp. 31 and 33**
- **Session 1.3, p. 38**
- **Session 1.4, p. 43**
- **Session 2.1, pp. 57 and 59**
- **Session 2.2, pp. 62 and 63**
- **Session 2.3, pp. 72 and 73**
- **Session 2.4, p. 78**
- **Session 2.5, p. 83**
- **Session 3.1, pp. 92 and 96**
- **Session 3.2, pp. 99 and 102**
- **Session 3.3, p. 106**
- **Session 3.4, pp. 112 and 113**

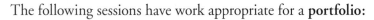

WRITING OPPORTUNITIES

The following sessions have **writing** opportunities for students to explain their mathematical thinking:

- **Session 1.1, p. 24**
  Student Activity Book, p. 1
- **Session 1.1, p. 27**
  Student Activity Book, p. 3
- **Session 2.3, p. 69**
  Student Activity Book, p. 10
- **Session 2.4, p. 78**
  Student Activity Book, p. 12
- **Session 3.3, p. 106**
  Student Activity Book, p. 19

PORTFOLIO OPPORTUNITIES

The following sessions have work appropriate for a **portfolio:**

- **Session 1.1, p. 24**
  Student Activity Book, p. 1
- **Session 1.1, p. 27**
  Student Activity Book, p. 3
- **Session 2.3, p. 69**
  Student Activity Book, p. 10
- **Session 2.4, p. 78**
  Student Activity Book, p. 12
- **Session 2.5, p. 83**
  M11, Assessment: "Deep Sea or Outer Space?" Representations
- **Session 3.4, pp. 111–113**
  M13–M15, End-of-Unit Assessment

Assessing the Benchmarks

Observing students as they engage in conversation about their ideas is a primary means to assess their mathematical understanding. Consider all of your students' work, not just the written assessments. See the chart below for suggestions about key activities to observe.

See the **Differentiation and Intervention Guide** for quizzes that can be used after each Investigation.

Benchmarks in This Unit	Key Activities to Observe	Assessment
1. Sort a group of objects according to a given attribute.	**Session 1.2:** Sorting Buttons **Session 1.3:** *Guess My Rule*	**Session 3.4 End-of-Unit Assessment:** Problem 1 **Session 1.3, 1.4:** Sorting ☑
2. Represent a set of data with two categories.	**Session 2.4:** Representing Survey Data **Session 2.5:** Sharing Survey Results **Session 3.1:** Representations of Our Ages	**Session 2.5 Assessment Activity:** "Deep Sea or Outer Space?" Representations
3. Interpret a variety of data representations with two categories.	**Sessions 1.1, 1.2, 2.1, 2.2, 3.1, 3.2, 3.3, 3.4:** *Quick Survey* **Session 2.4:** Representing Survey Data **Session 2.5:** Sharing Survey Results **Session 3.3:** Us and Our Siblings	**Session 2.5 Assessment Activity:** "Deep Sea or Outer Space?" Representations **Session 3.4 End-of-Unit Assessment:** Problems 2 and 3
4. Describe a set of data, including how many are in each group, which group is greater, and how many people responded to the survey.	**Session 2.4:** Representing Survey Data **Session 2.5:** Sharing Survey Results	**Session 3.4 End-of-Unit Assessment:** Problems 2 and 3

 Checklist Available

Relating the Mathematical Emphases to the Benchmarks

Mathematical Emphases	Benchmarks
Data Analysis Sorting and Classifying	1
Data Analysis Representing Data	2
Data Analysis Describing and Interpreting Data	3, 4
Data Analysis Designing and Carrying Out a Data Investigation	2, 3, 4

Classroom Routines

Classroom Routines offer practice and review of key concepts for this grade level. These daily activities, to be done in ten minutes outside of math class, occur in a regular rotation every 4–5 days. Specific directions for the day's routine are provided in each session. For the full description and variations of each classroom routine see *Implementing Investigations in Grade 1*.

Morning Meeting

Students continue to use the calendar to keep track of time and events, collect and analyze data about the weather, and count the number of students in the class. Variations focus on using the calendar to solve problems, and discussing the yearly weather data.

Math Focus Points

◆ Collecting and recording data

◆ Using the calendar as a tool for keeping track of time

◆ Developing strategies for counting accurately

◆ Developing vocabulary to talk about time (*morning, noon, midday, afternoon,* etc.) and sequence (*first, next, last, before, after,* etc.)

◆ Making sense of a variety of representations of data

Quick Images: Coins

Students see groups of coins. They determine the total amount and identify the type of each coin.

Math Focus Points

◆ Identifying and naming coins

◆ Developing and analyzing visual images for quantities

Start With/Get To

Students practice counting forward and backward with numbers to 60. Then, students count *from* a number between 0 and 30 *to* a number between 31–60 keeping track of the numbers on the 100 chart.

Math Focus Points

◆ Practicing the forward and backward counting sequences with numbers up to 60

◆ Using the number line as a tool for counting

◆ Using the 100 chart as a tool for counting

◆ Connecting written numbers and number names

Practice and Review

IN THIS UNIT

Practice and review play a critical role in the *Investigations* program. The following components and features are available to provide regular reinforcement of key mathematical concepts and procedures.

Books	Features	In This Unit ...
Curriculum Unit	**Classroom Routines** offer practice and review of key concepts for this grade level. These daily activities, to be done in ten minutes outside of math class, occur in a regular rotation every 4–5 days. Specific directions for the day's routine are provided in each session. For the full description and variations of each classroom routine see *Implementing Investigations in Grade 1*.	• **All sessions**
Student Activity Book	**Daily Practice** pages in the *Student Activity Book* provide one of three types of written practice: **reinforcement** of the content of the unit, **ongoing review,** or **enrichment** opportunities. Some Daily Practice pages will also have Ongoing Review items with multiple-choice problems similar to those on standardized tests.	• **All sessions**
	Homework pages in the *Student Activity Book* are an extension of the work done in class. At times they help students prepare for upcoming activities.	• **Session 1.1** • **Session 3.3** • **Session 2.4** • **Session 3.2**
Student Math Handbook	**Math Words and Ideas** in the *Student Math Handbook* are pages that summarize key words and ideas. Most Words and Ideas pages have at least one exercise.	• **Student Math Handbook, pp. 17–18, 24–29, 33–41, 64–68, 76–79**
	Games pages are found in a section of the *Student Math Handbook*.	• **Student Math Handbook, p. G12**

Differentiation

IN THIS UNIT

Supporting the Range of Learners

The **Differentiation and Intervention Guide** provides Intervention, Extension, and Practice activities for use within each Investigation.

Sessions	1.1	1.2	1.3	1.4	2.3	2.4	3.1	3.2	3.4
Intervention	•	•	•		•	•	•	•	
Extension				•					
ELL	•				•				•

Intervention

Suggestions are made to support and engage students who are having difficulty with a particular idea, activity, or problem.

Extension

Suggestions are made to support and engage students who finish early or may be ready for additional challenge.

English Language Learners (ELL)

Because so many of the activities are language-based, English Language Learners may need extra support in order to grasp the concepts about data that are presented, explored, and discussed throughout this unit.

After sorting a group of objects according to their attributes, English Language Learners might have trouble explaining how they sorted them. You can help by asking them to show you how the objects are the same and then telling them the word in English that describes how they are the same: *round, 4 sides, blue,* and so on. Work with a small group of English Language Learners to sort a set of Power Polygons according to different attributes, such as, size and shape. It might be helpful to refer to the chart you created of words describing Power Polygons, and work together to sort some Power Polygons using the words on the chart. You can also work with them to add more words to the chart.

English Language Learners must also learn data-related terms such as *survey, question, response,* and *data.* To reinforce this vocabulary, you can gather English Language Learners in a small group and do a survey with them, record their responses and ask them to describe and show what they notice.

Working with the Range of Learners: Classroom Cases is a set of episodes written by teachers that focuses on meeting the needs of the range of learners in the classroom. In the first section, *Setting up the Mathematical Community,* teachers write about how they create a supportive and productive learning environment in their classrooms. In the next section, *Accommodations for Learning,* teachers focus on specific modifications they make to meet the needs of some of their learners. In the last section, *Language and Representation,* teachers share how they help students use representations and develop language to investigate and express mathematical ideas. The questions at the end of each case provide a starting point for your own reflection or for discussion with colleagues. See *Implementing Investigations in Grade 1* for this set of episodes.

Mathematical Emphases

Data Analysis Sorting and classifying

Math Focus Points

◆ Describing attributes of objects

◆ Using attributes to sort a set of objects

◆ Looking carefully at a group of objects to determine how they have been sorted

Data Analysis Representing data

Math Focus Points

◆ Making a representation to communicate the results of a survey

Data Analysis Designing and carrying out a data investigation

Math Focus Points

◆ Interpreting results of a data investigation

Sorting

SESSION 1.1 p. 22	Student Activity Book	Student Math Handbook	Professional Development: Read Ahead of Time
Sorting Shapes Students collect, record, and discuss responses to a survey question. They describe the attributes of selected shapes and sort them according to a specific attribute.	1–3	64, 76–77	• **Mathematics in This Unit,** p. 10 • **Teacher Note:** Sorting and Classifying, p. 115 • **Dialogue Box:** They're All Different Sizes, p. 135
SESSION 1.2 p. 28			
Sorting Buttons Students describe the attributes of buttons and sort them according to a specific attribute. They make representations of how they sorted the buttons.	3, 5	64	
SESSION 1.3 p. 34			
Guess My Rule Students sort objects according to their attributes as they play *Guess My Rule* with a variety of collections of objects.	6	64, 78–79; G12	• **Teacher Note:** *Guess My Rule,* p. 117 • **Dialogue Box:** *Guess My Rule* with Partners, p. 137
SESSION 1.4 p. 40			
Guess My Rule with People Students continue to play *Guess My Rule* with collections of objects. Then they play *Guess My Rule* with classmates and discuss ways to represent how they sorted them.	7	64, 78–79	

Classroom Routines See page 16 for an overview.

Morning Meeting
- **Yearly weather data chart**

Start With/Get To
- *Start with/Get to* **cards 1–60**
- **One basket, and a class number line**

Quick Images: Coins
- **Set of overhead coins**

Materials to Gather	Materials to Prepare
• **Self-stick notes** (as needed) • **Power Polygons** (20 per pair)	• **M1–M2, Family Letter** Make copies. (1 per student) • *Quick Survey* **Chart: "Milk"** Write the title "Will you drink milk with your lunch today?" on a piece of chart paper. Make a chart with two columns, one labeled "Yes" and one "No." See page 23 for an example. • **Chart paper** Title a piece of chart paper, "Shapes."
• **Self-stick notes** (as needed) • **Button collections** (1 set of about 20–25 per pair) • **Blank paper** (1 per pair) • **Markers or crayons** • **Glue** (optional)	• **Chart paper** Title a piece of chart paper, "Buttons". • *Quick Survey* **Chart: "Cup or Cone?"** Title a piece of chart paper "Which do you like better: frozen yogurt in a cup or in a cone?" Write "cup" and, a few spaces under it, write "cone". See page 32 for an example.
• **T32, These Fit My Rule** 🖥 • **T33, These Don't Fit My Rule** 🖥 • **Buttons** (3 sets of 20–25) • **Chart: Buttons** (from Session 1.2) • **Power Polygons** (3 sets of 20–25) • **Shells** (3 sets of 20–25)	• **M5, *Guess My Rule*** Make copies. (as needed) • **M6, These Fit My Rule** Make copies. (1 per student) • **M7, These Don't Fit My Rule** Make copies. (1 per student) • **M8, Assessment Checklist: Sorting** ☑ Make several copies per class. • **Collection of like objects** (3 sets of 20–25) Create a collection of like objects that can be sorted, such as keys, bottle caps, rocks, lids, or animal counters. Organize this collection in sets of 20–25 each and put them in plastic bags or small containers.
• **M6, These Fit My Rule** (1 per student; from Session 1.3) • **M7, These Don't Fit My Rule** (1 per student; from Session 1.3) • **M8, Assessment Checklist: Sorting** ☑ (several per class; from Session 1.3) • **Buttons** (3 sets of 20–25; from Session 1.3) • **Power Polygons** (3 sets of 20–25; from Session 1.3) • **Shells** (3 sets of 20–25; from Session 1.3) • **Collection of like objects** (3 sets of 20–25; from Session 1.3) • **Chart paper** (optional)	• **M3–M4, Family Letter** Make copies. (1 per student)

🖥 Overhead Transparency   ☑ Checklist Available

Sorting Shapes

Math Focus Points
- Describing attributes of objects
- Using attributes to sort a set of objects
- Interpreting results of a data investigation

Vocabulary
survey
data
sorting
describe
attribute

Today's Plan		Materials
ACTIVITY **1** *Quick Survey:* Milk	10 MIN · CLASS	• *Quick Survey* Chart: "Milk"*; self-stick notes
ACTIVITY **2** Describing Shapes	15 MIN · CLASS · PAIRS	• *Student Activity Book*, p. 1 • Power Polygons
DISCUSSION **3** Describing Shapes	20 MIN · CLASS	• Chart: "Shapes"; self-stick notes; Power Polygons • Completed *Student Activity Book*, p. 1
ACTIVITY **4** Sorting Shapes	15 MIN · PAIRS	• Power Polygons
SESSION FOLLOW-UP **5** Daily Practice and Homework		• *Student Activity Book*, pp. 2–3 • *Student Math Handbook*, pp. 64, 76–77 • M1–M2, Family Letter*

*See *Materials to Prepare*, p. 21.

Classroom Routines

Start With/Get To: Forward or Backward? In this variation, there is one basket that holds all of the numbers (cards 1–60). Choose both the *start with* and *get to* numbers from this basket. Ask students to find and mark both numbers on the number line. Decide as a class if you will be counting forward or backward (up or down). As a class, count from the *start with* number to the *get to* number.

ACTIVITY

① *Quick Survey:* Milk

10 MIN   CLASS

Many of the sessions in this unit begin with a *Quick Survey* in which students collect and record data about a given question. The purpose of *Quick Survey* is to provide students with a number of short opportunities to participate in collecting, recording, and discussing data and to allow them to see a variety of ways to record data. ❶ ❷

Each *Quick Survey* activity includes a question, a recording method, and discussion questions. No more than ten minutes should be spent on a *Quick Survey*.

Post the *Quick Survey* chart "Milk" (prepared ahead of time) and introduce the survey to students.

Students write their names on self-stick notes and place the self-stick notes under "Yes" or "No" to indicate their answers to the following question:

Will you drink milk with your lunch today?

After recording students' responses, briefly discuss the survey. Use the following questions to help guide the discussion:

- What does this survey tell us about our class?

- Which group has the most? The fewest? How many people responded to the survey?

Teaching Note

❸ *Quick Survey* **Chart** Keep the *Quick Survey* chart "Milk" displayed in the room for students to refer to later. You may need to tape on the self-stick notes so that they do not fall off.

Differentiation

❹ **English Language Learners** You may want to preview this activity with English Language Learners prior to this session to give them time to think of words to describe the shapes. If an English Language Learner is unsure of how to say something, the student can point to the feature he or she wishes to describe, and you can provide the necessary language. During the activity, you can pair each English Language Learner with a student who is more proficient in English. Encourage the students to take turns writing down the words.

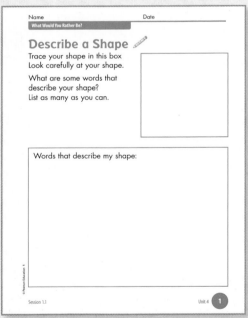

▲ **Student Activity Book, p. 1**

• How do you think doing this survey might be helpful to me? Why do you think it might be helpful to people working in our cafeteria?

• Why do you think [more students will drink milk today]? Do you think we'd get similar data if we collected it on a different day? What if we conducted the same survey in another classroom? Would the results be the same or different?

During the next few weeks, we're going to be working with data. We'll collect plenty of data by asking and responding to survey questions like the one I just asked you and showing and talking about the data we collected.❸

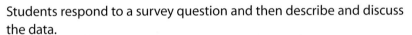

ONGOING ASSESSMENT: Observing Students at Work

Students respond to a survey question and then describe and discuss the data.

• **What types of observations and comments do students make about the data?**

• **Are they able to count the number of responses and total number of data?**

ACTIVITY

2 Describing Shapes

15 MIN   CLASS   PAIRS

Today we'll be sorting shapes. We'll think about how things are alike or different. For example, maybe you've helped someone in your family sort the laundry into white clothing and dark clothing. White clothing goes in one pile to be washed; dark clothing goes in another pile.

Spread 20 Power Polygons out on the floor or on an overhead so that all students can see them.

What do you notice about these shapes? How would you describe some of them?

Students may describe the shapes in terms of color, size, number of sides, or material (such as plastic), or other features.

I am going to give each pair of students one shape. For the next few minutes, you and your partner are going to think of as many words as you can that describe your shape, and then you are going to write the words on *Student Activity Book* page 1.❹

ONGOING ASSESSMENT: Observing Students at Work

Students describe attributes of a shape.

- **How do students describe their shapes?** Do they describe a range of attributes such as size, color, shape, and number of sides?

- **Do students know the name of their shape?**

DISCUSSION

③ Describing Shapes

20 MIN   CLASS

Math Focus Points for Discussion

◆ Describing attributes of objects

Ask each pair to share one of the words they used to describe a shape. Write each word on a separate self-stick note and place each self-stick note on the chart paper labeled "Shapes."

After all the pairs have shared one word, look at the words on the chart. Choose one attribute⑤ that many students described (e.g., color, size, number of sides, name, material).⑥

I noticed that many of you described the color of your shape. Which words describe the colors of the shapes?

In the upper left-hand corner of the chart, write *Color* and then place all the self-stick notes that describe color near *Color*.

When you described the color of the shapes, you were describing one of the attributes of that shape.

Discuss another attribute, such as size.

I noticed that some people said that their shapes were small or big. These words describe the sizes of the shapes. What other words describe the sizes of the shapes?

Write *Size* in the lower left-hand corner of the chart. Then place all the self-stick notes that describe size near *Size*.

We've talked about the [color and size] of the shapes. Now let's look at the rest of the words to figure out which ones go together and what they describe.

Math Note

⑤ **Attributes** An attribute is a characteristic, or way you can sort a group of things. For example, hair color, height, and gender are attributes of children.

Professional Development

⑥ **Dialogue Box:** They're All Different Sizes, p. 135

Teaching Note

❼ **Distinguishing Attributes** Some students may be able to identify the words that go together but unable to name the attribute they described. Work together to figure out the attribute, or tell students the name of the attribute.

Professional Development

❽ **Teacher Note:** Sorting and Classifying, p. 115

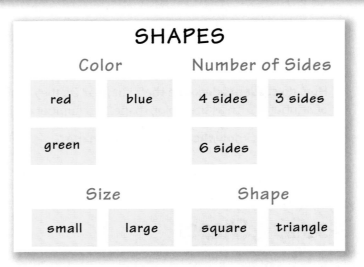

SHAPES

Color		Number of Sides	
red	blue	4 sides	3 sides
green		6 sides	

Size		Shape	
small	large	square	triangle

Decide together how to organize and name the attributes for students' other descriptions.❼ Other attributes might include these:

- Number of sides
- Shape
- Number of corners

Sort the rest of the self-stick notes by the attributes the class decided on.

15 MIN PAIRS

ACTIVITY

4 Sorting Shapes

Give each pair of students a set of 20 Power Polygons.

You are going to work with a partner to choose one of the attributes we have listed on the chart. Then you'll sort all your shapes by that attribute. You can choose to sort your shapes by color, size, number of sides, shape, or number of corners.

When students have finished, they should have shapes grouped according to the attribute they chose. For example, if they sorted by number of sides, they might have a group of shapes with six sides, a group of shapes with four sides, and a group of shapes with three sides.

Ask students to keep their shapes sorted in the area where they have been working. Each pair walks around the room to see how other pairs sorted their shapes. Ask them to guess how each set of shapes was sorted.❽

ONGOING ASSESSMENT: Observing Students at Work

Students sort shapes according to a specific attribute.

- **Are students able to sort the shapes according to the attribute they chose?** For example, are students able to sort by color or size?

- **Are students able to identify how the shapes they group together are the same?** If they sorted by color, can they identify that a group contains only blue shapes? If they sorted with size as the attribute, can they identify that a group contains only small shapes?

- **What do students do with shapes that don't seem to fit into any groups or that fit into more than one group?**

DIFFERENTIATION: Supporting the Range of Learners

Intervention After students have chosen an attribute, they may have difficulty figuring out how to group their shapes. To help them ask questions such as:

- If you are sorting by size, one of your groups may be big shapes. What might another group be?

You may also sort the shapes and ask students to identify the groups you sorted the shapes into and the attribute by which you sorted the shapes.

SESSION FOLLOW-UP
5 Daily Practice and Homework

 Daily Practice: For ongoing review, have students complete *Student Activity Book* page 2.

 Homework: Ask students to draw or tape a button on *Student Activity Book* page 3 and to list as many words as they can to describe their buttons. Students may ask family members to help them write the words.

 Student Math Handbook: Students and families may use *Student Math Handbook* pages 64, 76–77 for reference and review. See pages 145–152 in the back of this unit.

 Family Letter: Send home copies of the Family Letter (M1–M2).

What Is Missing?
Fill in the missing numbers.

NOTE Students practice writing numbers and work with the order of numbers from 1 to 100.

1	2	3	4		6	7		9	10
	12	13		15		17		19	
21		23	24	25				29	30
31	32				36				40
			44		46	47	48	49	
	52	53		55					60
			64			67		69	
71	72	73					78		
	82			85	86		88	89	
91	92		94			97			

Ongoing Review
How many flowers in all?

12   10   5   2
Ⓐ   Ⓑ   Ⓒ   Ⓓ

▲ Student Activity Book, p. 2

Describe a Button
Find a button. Look carefully at your button.

What are some words that describe your button?

List as many as you can.   Draw or tape your button here.

NOTE Students describe the attributes of a button, such as its size, shape, and color. We will use this homework for an activity in our next math session.

Words that describe my button:

▲ Student Activity Book, p. 3

Sorting Buttons

Math Focus Points

◆ Describing attributes of objects

◆ Using attributes to sort a set of objects

◆ Interpreting results of a data investigation

Today's Plan		Materials
① DISCUSSION **Describing Buttons**	🕐 20 MIN 👥 CLASS	• *Student Activity Book*, p. 3 (from Session 1.1) • Button Chart*; self-stick notes; buttons
② ACTIVITY **Sorting Buttons**	🕐 30 MIN 👥 PAIRS	• Button collections; blank paper; markers or crayons; glue (optional)
③ ACTIVITY ***Quick Survey:* Cup or Cone?**	🕐 10 MIN 👥 CLASS	• *Quick Survey* Chart: "Cup or Cone?"*
④ SESSION FOLLOW-UP **Daily Practice**		• *Student Activity Book*, p. 5 • *Student Math Handbook*, p. 64

*See *Materials to Prepare*, p. 21.

Classroom Routines

Start With/Get To: Forward or Backward? **Choose both the *start with* and *get to*** numbers from a basket holding the numbers 1 to 60. Ask students to find and mark both numbers on the number line. Decide as a class if you will be counting forward or backward (up or down). As a class, count from the *start with* number to the *get to* number.

DISCUSSION
①Describing Buttons

20 MIN   CLASS

Math Focus Points for Discussion

◆ Describing attributes of objects

During the last session you described the attributes of shapes. Today we're going to describe some attributes of buttons.

Using their homework from the previous session as a reference, ask each student to share a word that describes a button.❶ As with the shapes, write each word on a self-stick note and put it on the chart paper labeled "Buttons."

You described some different attributes of these buttons. I noticed that some of you talked about the number of holes. Which of these words describes the number of holes?

In the upper left-hand corner of the chart, write "Number of Holes." Then place all the self-stick notes that students say describe the number of holes under this heading.

Choose two other description words that go together.

I've noticed that some people use the word [red] to describe their button and other people use the word [yellow]. What other words go with [red or yellow]? What are you describing when you talk about a button being [red or yellow or green]?

Decide together on how to categorize students' other descriptions of the buttons.❷ Some attributes might include these:

• Material

• Size

• Texture (bumpy, smooth)

• Shape

• Color

• Number of holes

Sort the rest of the self-stick notes according to the attributes you came up with together. Then review attributes that the class used to sort the self-stick notes. Keep the chart posted for the next session.

Teaching Notes

❶ **Homework** If you did not assign *Student Activity Book* page 3, or if students have not brought it in, provide students with buttons that they can use during the discussion.

❷ **Distinguishing Attributes** Students may be able to say which words go together but may not be able to come up with the name of the attribute. For example, they may know that small and large go together, but they cannot come up with an attribute that fits both of those words. You might work on coming up with the attribute words together or provide some of them yourself.

BUTTONS

Number of Holes		Color	
4 holes	2 holes	red	blue
1 hole		green	

Size		Material	
small	large	plastic	metal
		wood	

ACTIVITY

2 Sorting Buttons

30 MIN   PAIRS

Yesterday you sorted shapes by an attribute you chose, such as number of sides or color. Today you're going to do the same thing with buttons. You'll sort the buttons by an attribute you choose from our chart, such as color, shape, or material.

After you've finished sorting, you'll show on a piece of paper *how* you sorted the buttons. What could you put on the paper so that someone looking at it would know how you sorted the buttons?

Students may talk about organizing them in groups, naming the groups, or writing the attribute by which the buttons are sorted on the paper. If any of these are not brought up, bring them up yourself.

Students might say:

"You can make a small group, a big group, and a medium group. Then you can draw the small buttons, the big buttons, and the medium buttons."

"You can put circles around your groups."

"You can write 4 for four holes and 2 for two holes and 1 for one hole."

Give each pair of students a set of buttons, a sheet of paper, markers or crayons, and glue (if they are gluing the buttons down).❸

Remind students of the attributes they came up with by looking again at the chart they just made. They should sort all of the buttons according to the attribute they chose.

Before students glue their buttons down (or draw them), you should ask each pair how they sorted their buttons. Then, ask them to tell you about their categories. Remind them that they should show on their paper how they sorted the buttons so that someone else can look at their paper and tell how they sorted them.

Students show on paper how they sorted buttons into groups, using attributes such as number of holes.

ONGOING ASSESSMENT: Observing Students at Work

Students sort buttons according to a specific attribute and make representations of how they sorted the buttons.

- **Are students able to sort the buttons according to the attribute they chose (size, color, number of holes)?**

- **Are students able to identify how the buttons they grouped together are the same?** For example, if they sorted by color, can they identify that a group contains only blue buttons? If they sorted by size, can they identify that a group contains only small buttons?

Teaching Notes

❹ *Quick Survey* Read the *Quick Survey* activity in Session 1.1 (page 23) for information on how to structure the surveys, their purpose, and some suggestions for other survey questions.

❺ *Quick Survey* **Chart** Keep the *Quick Survey* chart "Cup or Cone?" displayed in the room for students to refer to later. You may need to tape on the self-stick notes so that they do not fall off.

- **What do students do with buttons that do not seem to fit into any groups or that fit in more than one group?** For example, what does a student who is sorting by color do with a button with both blue and white colors?

- **Are students able to make a representation that shows clearly how they sorted their buttons?**

- **Do students name and label the sorted groups?** For example, do they label groups sorted by color names such as *Blue* and *Red*?

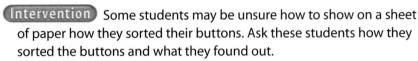

DIFFERENTIATION: Supporting the Range of Learners

Intervention Some students may be unsure how to show on a sheet of paper how they sorted their buttons. Ask these students how they sorted the buttons and what they found out.

How can you show that you sorted your buttons by [color] and that you had [green, red, and blue] buttons?

ACTIVITY

③ *Quick Survey:* Cup or Cone?

10 MIN   CLASS

End the session by doing the following *Quick Survey.* ❹ Post the *Quick Survey* chart "Cup or Cone?" that you prepared ahead of time.

Which do you like better: frozen yogurt in a cup or frozen yogurt in a cone?

Draw a cup next to the word *Cup* for each student who prefers frozen yogurt in a cup and a cone next to the word *Cone* for each student who prefers frozen yogurt in a cone.

Which do you like better:
frozen yogurt in a cup or in a cone?

| Cup | ⊔⊔⊔⊔⊔⊔⊔⊔⊔ |
| Cone | ▽▽▽▽▽▽▽▽▽▽▽ ▽▽▽▽▽ |

After recording students' responses, have a short discussion about the results of the survey.⑤ Use questions such as the following to guide the discussion:

- What does this survey tell us about our class?

- How many people prefer frozen yogurt in a cup? How many prefer frozen yogurt in a cone? In our class, are there more people who like frozen yogurt in a cup or more people who like frozen yogurt in a cone? Are there many more people who like frozen yogurt in a cone or just a few more people?

- How many people responded to the survey?

- Do you think we'd get similar data if we asked this question on a different day? What if we did the same survey in another classroom? Would the data be the same or different?

Name _____ Date _____

What Would You Rather Be?   Daily Practice

Finding Socks

Jacob was cleaning his room.
He found 3 socks under his bed.
He found 6 socks in his closet.
He found 4 socks on the floor.
How many socks did he find in all?

NOTE Students combine three quantities to solve a story problem. 33–37

Solve the problem. Show your work.

Session 1.2   Unit 4 5

▲ **Student Activity Book, p. 5**

ONGOING ASSESSMENT: Observing Students at Work

Students respond to a survey question and then describe and discuss the data.

- **What types of observations do students make about the data?**

- **Are students able to count the number of responses in each category?** Can they determine the total number of responses?

- **What types of predictions do students make about collecting data?**

SESSION FOLLOW-UP

4 Daily Practice

 Daily Practice: For ongoing review, have students complete *Student Activity Book* page 5.

Student Math Handbook: Students and families may use *Student Math Handbook* page 64 for reference and review. See pages 145–152 in the back of this unit.

Guess My Rule

Math Focus Points

◆ Using attributes to sort a set of objects

◆ Looking carefully at a group of objects to determine how they have been sorted

Vocabulary

rule

Today's Plan		Materials
ACTIVITY **① Introducing** *Guess My Rule* **with Buttons**	🕐 **15 MIN** 👥 **CLASS**	• M5*; M6*, T32 🖨; M7*, T33 🖨 • Buttons (3 sets of 20–25); Buttons Chart (from Session 1.2)
MATH WORKSHOP **②** *Guess My Rule* **②A** *Guess My Rule* with Buttons **②B** *Guess My Rule* with Shapes **②C** *Guess My Rule* with Shells **②D** *Guess My Rule* with [Another Collection]	🕐 **35 MIN**	• M8 ☑ **②A** • M6*; M7* • Buttons (3 sets 20–25) **②B** • M6*; M7* • Power Polygons (3 sets of 20–25) **②C** • M6*; M7* • Shells (3 sets of 20–25) **②D** • M6*; M7* • Collection of like objects (3 sets of 20–25)
DISCUSSION **③** *Guess My Rule*	🕐 **10 MIN** 👥 **CLASS**	
SESSION FOLLOW-UP **④ Daily Practice**		• *Student Activity Book,* p. 6 • *Student Math Handbook,* pp. 64, 78–79; G12

*See *Materials to Prepare,* p. 21.

Classroom Routines

Morning Meeting: Discussing the Yearly Data **Follow your daily *Morning Meeting* Routine. During *Weather,* discuss the data that has been collected for the year. Choose a category and ask students to look at the data collected.**

How many days has it been [rainy] so far this year? How do you know?

Have students share their strategies.

ACTIVITY

Introducing *Guess My Rule* with Buttons

15 MIN · CLASS

Seat students where they can see one another and the buttons (if possible, students in a circle on the floor with the buttons in the middle). Place the buttons, These Fit My Rule (M6), and These Don't Fit My Rule (M7) where everyone can see them.❶

Today we are going to play a game called *Guess My Rule*. I am going to choose a rule that fits some of these buttons but not all of them. I am going to put the buttons that fit my rule on the sheet of paper that says "These Fit My Rule."

Hold up the These Fit My Rule sorting mat (M6).

I am going to put the buttons that don't fit my rule on the paper that says "These Don't Fit My Rule."

Hold up the These Don't Fit My Rule sorting mat (M7).

Choose a rule that fits some of the buttons but not all of them (such as red color). Write your rule on a scrap piece of paper and turn it over so that no one can see the rule.

I have written my rule on this piece of paper and turned it over so that no one can see. This will help me remember my rule.

Place two buttons that fit your rule on the These Fit My Rule sorting mat. Put two buttons that do not fit your rule on the These Don't Fit My Rule sorting mat.

These buttons fit my rule. They are alike in some way. These other buttons do not fit my rule. If you think you know my rule, don't say it yet! Instead, can you find another button that you think fits or doesn't fit my rule?

Give everyone a moment to look carefully at the buttons. Call on someone to choose another button to place on the paper where he or she thinks it belongs. Affirm whether it fits or does not fit the rule, and change its location as needed.

Professional Development

❶ **Teacher Note:** *Guess My Rule*, p. 117

▲ Resource Masters, M6; T32

▲ Resource Masters, M7; T33

Students add buttons to the These Fit My Rule and These Don't Fit My Rule sorting mats.

Have students continue taking turns until at least ten buttons have been placed. Then ask someone to guess the rule. All those who agree should raise their hands.

Many people are agreeing with Diego that my rule is *red* buttons. Who can explain why they think this is or isn't my rule?

Affirm whether this is the rule by showing students the paper with your rule on it. After the rule has been affirmed, ask a student to sort the rest of the buttons on to the two pieces of paper.

Play at least two more rounds with students. Some rules you might use include the following:

- Buttons with 4 holes

- Buttons with a ring on the edge

- Buttons with designs on them

- Buttons with two colors on them

- Buttons that are shiny

Point out that students can use the class chart of button attributes and description words (from Session 1.2) to help them figure out a good rule.

MATH WORKSHOP

② Guess My Rule

35 MIN

Explain to students that during Math Workshop they will be playing *Guess My Rule* with a variety of collections: buttons, shapes, shells, and a collection you have created.❷ Show students the three new collections and discuss briefly some possible rules they could use for these collections. Students will continue with these Math Workshop activities in Session 1.4 and will need to save These Fit My Rule (M6) and These Don't Fit My Rule (M7). While you observe students playing *Guess My Rule*, you can assess how students sort objects using attributes (Benchmark 1). Record your observations using the Assessment Checklist: Sorting (M8).

②A *Guess My Rule* with Buttons

PAIRS

Students follow the procedure on pages 35–36.

②B *Guess My Rule* with Shapes

PAIRS

Students follow the procedure on pages 35–36.

②C *Guess My Rule* with Shells

PAIRS

Students follow the procedure on pages 35–36.

②D *Guess My Rule* with [Another Collection]

PAIRS

Students follow the procedure on pages 35–36.

A student sorts a collection created by the teacher into groups that fit or do not fit the rule.

❷ **Dialogue Box:** *Guess My Rule* with Partners, p. 137

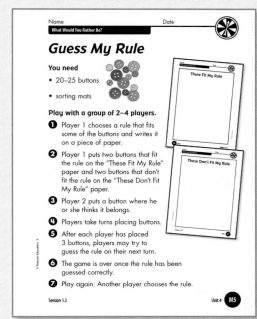

▲ **Resource Masters, M5**

❸ **Assessing Students as They Sort** As students play *Guess My Rule*, gather information about their ability to identify attributes of objects and sort objects into groups (Benchmark 1). This benchmark is also assessed in the End-of-Unit Assessment.

ONGOING ASSESSMENT: Observing Students at Work

As students play *Guess My Rule* in activities 2A–2D, they are sorting objects according to their attributes. They are also looking carefully at the objects to determine how they are being sorted.

- **Do students choose a rule that is clear and based on an observable characteristic?**

- **Do students correctly sort the objects according to that rule?**

- **Do students make systematic choices of objects to be placed on the basis of evidence from objects already sorted?**

Assessment Checklist: Sorting

Student	Identifies an attribute to sort a set of objects • Attribute pertains to some but not all of the objects • Attribute is identifiable by others	Sorts objects according to the identified attribute • Sorts objects accurately • Sorts objects consistently	Identifies the attribute by which a given set of objects has been sorted
Vic	buttons: 4 holes	✓	
Carol			buttons: purple (Libby's rule)
Teo	Power Polygons: squares	✓ Uses "not a rectangle" as a clue for partner	
Tamika	Power Polygons: 4 corners	✓ includes squares, rectangles, and rhombuses	
Marta	Power Polygons: blue (can she use a geometric rule?)	✓	
William			Power Polygons: blue (Marta's Rule)
Isabel (and Felipe)	buttons: small	discuss which buttons are small	

You can observe students doing any of the *Guess My Rule* activities and record your observations on Assessment Checklist: Sorting (M8).❸

DIFFERENTIATION: Supporting the Range of Learners

Intervention Some students may find it difficult to focus on only one attribute that a number of different objects have in common. For these students, sort a collection into groups and ask the students to identify how you sorted them. Then, ask them to sort a group of objects according to an attribute that you identify.

DISCUSSION
3 Guess My Rule

10 MIN CLASS

Math Focus Points for Discussion

◆ Looking carefully at a group of objects to determine how they have been sorted

During the last ten minutes of this session, have a discussion about a few difficulties or ideas that have come up as students played *Guess My Rule.*

Possible questions for discussion might include these:

- What rules worked well?
- What rules were more difficult to figure out?
- What was challenging as you played *Guess My Rule?*
- How does looking at the objects that don't fit the rule help you figure out what the rule is?
- For which collections was it harder to come up with rules? For which collections was it easier to come up with rules?

SESSION FOLLOW-UP
4 Daily Practice

Daily Practice: For ongoing review, have students complete *Student Activity Book* page 6.

Student Math Handbook: Students and families may use *Student Math Handbook* pages 64, 78–79 and G12 for reference and review. See pages 145–152 in the back of this unit.

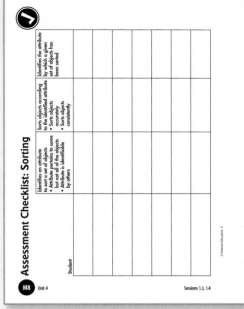

▲ Resource Masters, M8 ✓

▲ Student Activity Book, p. 6

Guess My Rule with People

Math Focus Points

◆ Using attributes to sort a set of objects

◆ Looking carefully at a group of objects to determine how they have been sorted

◆ Making a representation to communicate the results of a survey

Today's Plan		Materials
MATH WORKSHOP **❶ Guess My Rule** **⓵ⓐ** Guess My Rule with Buttons **⓵ⓑ** Guess My Rule with Shapes **⓵ⓒ** Guess My Rule with Shells **⓵ⓓ** Guess My Rule with [Another Collection]	🕐 30 MIN	• M8 ☑ * **⓵ⓐ** • M6*; M7* • Buttons (3 sets of 20–25) **⓵ⓑ** • M6*; M7* • Power Polygons (3 sets of 20–25) **⓵ⓒ** • M6*; M7* • Shells (3 sets of 20–25) **⓵ⓓ** • M6*; M7* • Collection of like objects (3 sets of 20–25)*
ACTIVITY **❷ Guess My Rule with People**	🕐 20 MIN 👥 CLASS	
DISCUSSION **❸ Guess My Rule Representation**	🕐 10 MIN 👥 CLASS	• Chart paper (optional)
SESSION FOLLOW-UP **❹ Daily Practice**		• Student Activity Book, p. 7 • Student Math Handbook, pp. 64, 78–79 • M3–M4, Family Letter*

*See Materials to Prepare, p. 21.

Classroom Routines

Quick Images: Coins Using the set of overhead coins, display 2 pennies and 2 nickels in groups of two. Follow the basic *Quick Images* activity. Discuss the quantity and type of coins with the class. Ask questions that focus on identifying each coin and the total number of coins.

Which coin is the [penny]? What is the name of *this* coin? How many [nickels] did you see? How do you know?

If time permits, repeat using 2 dimes and 2 quarters. For a full write-up of this variation, see *Implementing Investigations in Grade 1*.

MATH WORKSHOP

1 Guess My Rule

30 MIN

Students continue to play *Guess My Rule* with buttons, Power Polygons, shells, and the collection you have created. Students should play *Guess My Rule* with a collection they did not use during the last session.❶

Continue to assess students' ability to identify attributes of objects and to sort objects into groups. As you observe any of the Math Workshop activities, record your observations on Assessment Checklist: Sorting (M8).

1A *Guess My Rule* with Buttons

PAIRS

For complete details about this activity, see Session 1.3, pages 35–37.

1B *Guess My Rule* with Shapes

PAIRS

For complete details about this activity, see Session 1.3, pages 35–37.

1C *Guess My Rule* with Shells

PAIRS

For complete details about this activity, see Session 1.3, pages 35–37.

1D *Guess My Rule* with [Another Collection]

PAIRS

For complete details about this activity, see Session 1.3, pages 35–37.

Students continue to play Guess My Rule *with Power Polygons.*

Teaching Note

❷ *Guess My Rule* **with People** This is a good game to play anytime during the school day when you have a few extra minutes to spare.

DIFFERENTIATION: Supporting the Range of Learners

Extension Students who can easily play *Guess My Rule* with one rule can play *Guess My Rule* with two rules. To play *Guess My Rule* with two rules, one person decides on two rules to use to sort a collection (e.g., buttons that are both round and red). Students put the objects that fit both rules in one group and objects that do not fit both rules in another group. For example, if the rules are that the buttons are round and red, buttons that are both round and red would be placed on the These Fit My Rule sheet, and those that are not both round and red would be placed on the These Don't Fit My Rule sheet.

ACTIVITY
2 *Guess My Rule* with People

20 MIN CLASS

We are going to play another version of *Guess My Rule.* This time we're going to play *Guess My Rule* with students in this class. I am going to think of a rule that fits some of you but not all of you. I am going to write down my rule so that I don't forget it, and I'm going to keep it secret for now.❷

Choose a straightforward, visually obvious rule (such as wearing stripes) that fits some of the students.

I am going to ask the students who fit my rule to stand over here, and the students who don't fit my rule to stand over there.

Ask two participants who fit your rule to stand in one part of the room. Ask two participants who do not fit your rule to stand in another part of the room.

These two people fit my rule. These two people do not fit my rule. Don't try to guess my rule yet. Instead, can you tell me someone who you think might fit my rule or someone who you think doesn't fit my rule?

The teacher has chosen a rule that fits some students and not others. The class tries to figure out the teacher's rule.

Students take turns suggesting class members they think fit the rule. Either affirm that the person fits the rule, or ask the student to stand with the "does not fit the rule" group. If no one names a student they think does *not* fit the rule, ask:

Is there anyone you think does not fit my rule? Finding out who doesn't fit my rule is just as important as finding out who does fit the rule. It gives you important information that will help you figure out the rule.

Students continue suggesting people who they think do or do not fit the rule until most of the students have been sorted. Ask for volunteers to share what they think the rule is and to tell why they think that is the rule. Affirm the rule by showing your paper and reading it aloud, and then record the rule on the board.

Play a few more rounds, first choosing the rule yourself and then asking for student volunteers to make a rule in consultation with you. Make sure that students understand that you are grouping people by a characteristic that everyone can see, such as *hair color* or *clothing,* not a characteristic that cannot be seen, such as *likes chocolate* or *has a dog.* After students guess a rule, record it on the board.

ONGOING ASSESSMENT: Observing Students at Work

Students sort a group of people according to visible attributes. They are also looking carefully at the people to determine how they are being sorted.

- **Do students choose a rule that is clear and based on an observable characteristic?**

• **Do students correctly place people according to that rule?**

• **Are students able to identify and place people who do not fit the rule?**

DISCUSSION

③ *Guess My Rule* Representation

10 MIN CLASS

Math Focus Points for Discussion

◆ Making a representation to communicate the results of a survey

Choose one of the rules you used to play *Guess My Rule* with people. Sort all the students in the class again by that rule.

What if we wanted to show someone who is not in this class what we found out about students in this class who [were wearing buttons today] and students who [were not wearing buttons today]? How could we show what we found out on a sheet of paper?

Take two or three suggestions for ways to represent the data you collected from your round of *Guess My Rule*. For example, students might suggest drawing a chart with the people who wore buttons in one column and the people who did not in another column, or making a chart with circles (for students with buttons) and Xs (for students without buttons). Students are also likely to suggest using numbers to show how many there are in the "with buttons" group.

It is important to choose two or three ways of representing this data. Representations should show how many students are in each category and include examples with or without numbers. If students do not come up with representations that fit these criteria, help clarify what you are looking for by asking the following questions:

• How could we show that 10 people were wearing buttons and 15 people were not wearing buttons?

• How could we use pictures?

• How could we show this information without using pictures?

• How can we tell the difference between the number of people wearing buttons and those not wearing buttons?

Represent the data on chart paper or the board, using the two or three ways they suggest.

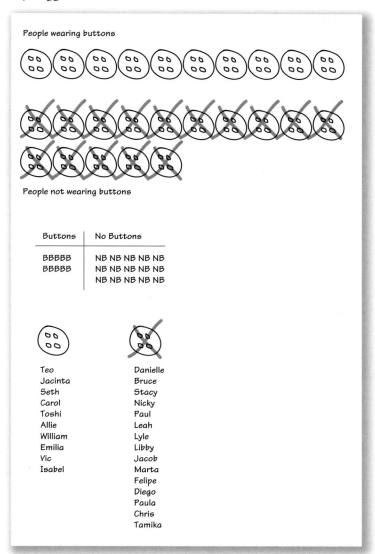

During the next few days you are going to be collecting plenty of different information. After you collect the information, you are going to find ways to show other people what you have learned from the data, as we did today.

▲ Student Activity Book, p. 7

4 Daily Practice

Daily Practice: For reinforcement of this unit's content, have students complete *Student Activity Book* page 7.

Student Math Handbook: Students and families may use *Student Math Handbook* pages 64, 78–79 for reference and review. See pages 145–152 in the back of this unit.

Family Letter: Send home copies of the Family Letter (M3–M4).

Mathematical Emphases

Data Analysis Representing data

Math Focus Points

◆ Making a representation to communicate the results of a survey

◆ Making sense of data representations, including pictures, bar graphs, tallies, and Venn diagrams

◆ Comparing what different representations communicate about a set of data

◆ Using equations to show how the sum of the responses in each category equals the total responses collected

Data Analysis Describing data

Math Focus Points

◆ Describing and comparing the number of pieces of data in each category or at each value and interpreting what the data tell you about the group

Data Analysis Designing and carrying out a data investigation

Math Focus Points

◆ Choosing a survey question

◆ Making a plan for gathering data

◆ Collecting and keeping track of survey data

◆ Interpreting results of a data investigation

Collecting and Representing Data

	Student Activity Book	Student Math Handbook	Professional Development: Read Ahead of Time	
SESSION 2.1 p. 52				
What Would You Rather Be? Students respond to a survey question, Would You Rather Be an Eagle or a Whale?, and figure out ways to represent the data with cubes, drawings, or other materials.	8	65, 66, 68	• **Teacher Notes:** Describing Data, p. 122; Grade 1 Students' Representations of Data, p. 119 • **Dialogue Box:** Discussing "Eagle or Whale?" Data, p. 139	
SESSION 2.2 p.60				
"Eagle or Whale?" Representations Students finish their representations of the "Eagle or Whale?" data. They use their representations to help them describe the results of this survey.	9	65, 66, 67, 68		
SESSION 2.3 p. 67				
Surveys Students develop their own survey questions and make a plan for gathering the data. They collect and record classmates' responses to their surveys.	10–11	65, 66, 67, 68		

Classroom Routines See page 16 for an overview.

Morning Meeting
- No materials needed

Quick Images
- Set of overhead coins

Start With/Get To
- *Start With/Get To* Cards 1–60
- Two baskets
- Class number line
- Class 100 chart

Materials to Gather	Materials to Prepare
• T34, Pictures of an Eagle and a Whale • *Quick Survey* Charts: "Milk" and "Cup or Cone?" (from Sessions 1.1 and 1.2) • Container or tub of connecting cubes in two colors (10–20 of each color) • Self-stick notes (as needed) • Connecting cubes, stick-on dots, self-stick notes, crayons or markers, and other materials for making representations (as needed) • 12″ x 18″ paper (1 sheet per student)	• *Quick Survey* Chart: "Brushing Your Teeth" Write the title "Do you brush your teeth and then get dressed, or do you get dressed and then brush your teeth?" at the top of the chart paper. Draw a line partway down the page to make two columns. At the bottom of the left column, write "I brush my teeth, and then I get dressed." At the bottom of the right column, write "I get dressed, and then I brush my teeth." See page 58 for an example.
• Students "Eagle or Whale" data representations (from Session 2.1) • Connecting cubes, stick-on dots, self-stick notes, crayons or markers, and other materials for making representations (as needed) • 12″ x 18″ paper (1 sheet per student) • Collections for *Guess My Rule* (optional)	• *Quick Survey* Chart: "Left-Handed or Right-Handed?" Write the title "Are you left-handed or right-handed?" on a sheet of chart paper and then make a two-column chart. Label one column "Left-Handed" and the other "Right-Handed." See page 62 for an example.
• T35, Our Plan for Collecting Data • Materials for collecting data, such as connecting cubes and self-stick notes (as needed) • Clipboards (1 per pair; optional)	• Chart: "Choosing a Question" Put the following headings on a piece of chart paper: "Would you rather _____ or _____?"; "Which do you like better: _____ or _____?"; "Do you _____ or _____?"; "Which is harder for you: _____ or _____?"; "Are you _____ or _____?". Leave enough room under each heading for 4 or 5 examples. See page 68 for an example. • Planning Chart Write the title "How will you record students' answers?" at the top of a piece of chart paper. • Planning Chart Write the title "How will you make sure that you asked everyone?" at the top of a piece of chart paper. • Class list of students Make copies. (1 per student)

Overhead Transparency

Collecting and Representing Data, *continued*

SESSION 2.4 p. 75	Student Activity Book	Student Math Handbook	Professional Development: Read Ahead of Time	
Representing Survey Data Students make representations of their survey results. They analyze the data by answering questions about what they found out.	12–14	66, 68		
SESSION 2.5 p. 80				
Assessment: "Deep Sea or Outer Space?" Representations Students share their findings from their surveys with the class. They complete an assessment in which they represent the results of a survey and answer questions about the data.	12, 15	66, 68	• **Teacher Note:** Assessment: "Deep Sea or Outer Space?" Representations, p. 124 • **Dialogue Box:** Sharing Survey Findings, p. 141	

Materials to Gather	Materials to Prepare
• **Students' survey data** (from Session 2.3) • **12˝ x 18˝ paper** (1 sheet per student) • **Markers or crayons** • **Self-stick notes, stick-on dots, and other materials to make representations** • **Class list** (1 per student from Session 2.3; plus 1 copy for the teacher)	
• **Students' survey representations** (from Session 2.4)	• **M11, Assessment: "Deep Sea or Outer Space?" Representations** Make copies. (1 per student) • **Class List with "Deep Sea or Outer Space?" Representations Data** Make copies of the class list on which you recorded the responses to the "Deep Sea or Outer Space" question in the previous session. (1 per student)

What Would You Rather Be?

Math Focus Points

◆ Making a representation to communicate the results of a survey

◆ Using equations to show that the sum of the responses in each category equals the total responses collected

◆ Describing and comparing the number of pieces of data in each category or at each value and interpreting what the data tell you about the group

Vocabulary

survey
data
equation
representation

Today's Plan | Materials

① ACTIVITY **Collecting "Eagle or Whale?" Data** 10 MIN · CLASS		• *Quick Survey* Charts: "Milk" and "Cup or Cone?" (from Sessions 1.1 and 1.2) • T34, Pictures of an Eagle and a Whale • Container or tub of connecting cubes in two colors; self-stick notes
② DISCUSSION **Discussing "Eagle or Whale?" Data** 10 MIN · CLASS		
③ ACTIVITY **Representations of "Eagle or Whale?" Data** 30 MIN · INDIVIDUALS		• Connecting cube representation of "Eagle or Whale?" data; connecting cubes, stick-on dots, self-stick notes, crayons or markers, and other materials for making representations; 12″ x 18″ paper
④ ACTIVITY ***Quick Survey:* Brushing Your Teeth** 10 MIN · CLASS		• *Quick Survey* Chart: "Brushing Your Teeth"*
⑤ SESSION FOLLOW-UP **Daily Practice**		• *Student Activity Book,* p. 8 • *Student Math Handbook,* pp. 65, 66, 68

*See *Materials to Prepare,* p. 49.

Classroom Routines

Start With/Get To: Forward or Backward? **Choose both the *start with* and *get to* numbers from a basket holding the numbers 1 to 60. Ask students to find and mark both numbers on the number line. Decide as a class if you will be counting forward or backward (up or down). Have students take turns saying one number as they count their way around the circle from the *start with* to the *get to* number.**

ACTIVITY

Collecting "Eagle or Whale?" Data

10 MIN   CLASS

Two times in the last few days, I've asked all of you the same question about something and we recorded your responses and talked about them. These are called surveys. Does anyone remember what our surveys were about?

Point out the *Quick Survey* charts that are posted in the room.

Today we're going to do another survey, but after we talk about it, you're going to find your own way of showing your classmates' responses to the survey. Today our question is going to be about eagles and whales.

Show the class the transparency of Pictures of an Eagle and a Whale (T34), and ask students to describe these animals and share what they know about them. The amount of time you spend on this discussion will vary, depending on how familiar students are with these animals. When you are sure that students know what these animals are, pose the following survey question:

Suppose that you could be an eagle or a whale for one day. Which one would you rather be?

Give students a few minutes to think.

We are going to collect data about whether you would rather be eagles or whales. How could we use connecting cubes to keep track of our survey data?

Students are likely to suggest using one color to represent an "eagle" answer and another color to represent a "whale" answer. They may even suggest using particular colors that are associated with each animal. ❶

Choose one color to represent eagles and one to represent whales. Distribute a container with the selected colors of connecting cubes. Ask students to take a cube of one color if they would rather be eagles or one cube of the other color if they would rather be whales.

After each student has taken a cube, collect all of the connecting cubes for students who would rather be eagles and put them together in a tower. Take all of the connecting cubes for students who would rather be whales, and put them in another tower. Place these towers on the ledge of the board or in the middle of the circle. Use self-stick notes to label the tower of eagle responses "Eagles" and the other "Whales."

Teaching Notes

❶ **Undecided Students** If some students insist that they cannot decide whether they would like to be eagles or whales, decide with the class on a way to represent "undecided."

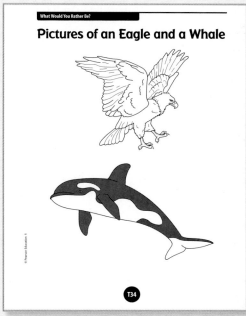

What Would You Rather Be?

Pictures of an Eagle and a Whale

T34

▲ Transparencies, T34

The teacher collected the cubes students used to designate whether they would rather be an eagle or a whale and puts them into two towers.

What do these towers tell us?

If no one mentions it, ask students about how many people wanted to be eagles and how many wanted to be whales.

Count the number of connecting cubes in each tower. Write the number of students who wanted to be eagles and the number who wanted to be whales on the board. Place the two towers of connecting cubes so students can see them.

DISCUSSION

❷ Discussing "Eagle or Whale?" Data

10 MIN   CLASS

Math Focus Points for Discussion

◆ Using equations to show that the sum of the responses in each category equals the total responses collected

◆ Describing and comparing the numbering of pieces of data in each category or at each value and interpreting what the data tell you about the group

How many people responded to the survey? How could we figure that out?

Students might say:

 "I know that there are 21 kids in the class and Libby is sick, so 20 people should have answered the survey."

 "You can count all the cubes."

 "I can add how many people said eagles and how many people said whales and that's how many people responded."

Math Note

❷ **Equations** Students may give examples of addition or subtraction equations that use the survey numbers. If students are not sure what the word *equation* means, give them some examples of addition or subtraction equations, such as $4 + 5 = 9$ or $6 - 3 = 3$.

Professional Development

❸ **Dialogue Box:** Discussing "Eagle or Whale?" Data, p. 139

❹ **Teacher Note:** Describing Data, p. 122

Use each of the different ways students suggest to figure out the total number of respondents. Write the total number of respondents on the board.

We know that [8] people would prefer to be eagles and [12] would prefer to be whales, and [20] people responded to the survey. Can anyone think of an equation❷ that shows this information?

Write the examples that fit your survey data on the board and label each part.

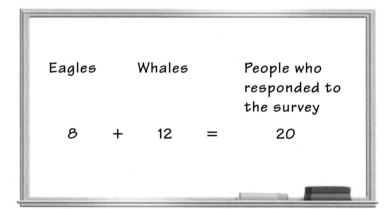

Eagles		Whales		People who responded to the survey
8	+	12	=	20

Finish this activity by asking students to share their reasoning for choosing to be eagles or whales.❸

Save the cube representation you made of the "Eagle or Whale?" data for students to refer to as they make their own representations in the next activity and as they discuss the representations at the end of the next session.❹

Teaching Note

⑤ Level of Detail Help students understand that they can communicate the data by using lines, checks, or simple pictures to represent people or whales, rather than creating detailed drawings.

ACTIVITY

③ Representations of "Eagle or Whale?" Data

30 MIN INDIVIDUALS

In a few minutes you are going to make your own **representation** of the "Eagle or Whale?" data. In other words, you are going to show in some way on your paper what we found out from our survey. Think about how you could show the "Eagle or Whale?" data so that someone who is not in this class could learn what we found out.

Show students the stick-on dots, connecting cubes, and other supplies you have gathered, and ask them how they might use these materials to show the results of the survey.

Students might suggest the following:⑤

- Drawing eagles and whales

- Using stick-on dots to indicate the responses in each group

- Drawing lines, checks, or other symbols to represent responses

Whatever materials you use, you need to show clearly what we found out so that other people can understand what we found out.

Remind students that they can look at the towers or the information you wrote on the board to help them remember how many people wanted to be eagles and how many wanted to be whales.

Distribute 12″ x 18″ sheets of paper, stick-on dots, crayons or markers, and other materials.

Sample Student Work

Some students may not be sure what to do because this is the first time they are making their own representations of data.❻ You might help them by asking questions.

What did you find out about whether the students in our class would rather be eagles or whales?

When it is clear that students understand what the results to the survey were, you might ask this question:

How could you show someone else who wasn't in our class what we found out?

After about 25 minutes, have students store their work and any unused materials. Let them know that they will continue working on their representations during the next session.

ONGOING ASSESSMENT: Observing Students at Work

Students organize and communicate data results as they create representations of class data.

- **Are students making representations that communicate the results of this survey clearly to others?**

- **Are students grouping the data that belong together?** Are students' categories distinct?

- **Do students accurately count the number of people who chose eagles and the number of people who chose whales?**

ACTIVITY

4 *Quick Survey:* Brushing Your Teeth

10 MIN   CLASS

At the end of this session, do the following *Quick Survey* with your students. ❼

In the morning, do you brush your teeth and then get dressed, or do you get dressed and then brush your teeth?

Professional Development

❻ **Teacher Note:** Grade 1 Students' Representations of Data, p. 119

Teaching Notes

❼ *Quick Survey* Read the *Quick Survey* activity in Session 1.1 (page 23) for information on how to structure the surveys, the purpose of these surveys, and suggestions for choosing survey questions.

Post the *Quick Survey* chart "Brushing Your Teeth" that you prepared, and record the survey results. Draw a face for each child's response above the corresponding words.

After recording students' responses, have a short discussion about the results of the survey. Use questions, such as the following, to guide the discussion:

- What does this survey tell us about our class?

- How many people brush their teeth and then get dressed? How many people get dressed and then brush their teeth?

- Are there more people who brush their teeth before getting dressed or more people who get dressed before brushing their teeth? Are there very many more? How many more?

- How many people responded to the survey?

Keep the *Quick Survey* chart "Brushing Your Teeth" posted for students to refer to later.

ONGOING ASSESSMENT: Observing Students at Work

Students respond to a survey question and then describe and discuss the data.

- **What types of observations and comments do students make about the data?**

- **Are they able to count the number of responses and total number of data?**

SESSION FOLLOW-UP
5 Daily Practice

 Daily Practice: For ongoing review, have students complete *Student Activity Book* page 8.

 Student Math Handbook: Students and families may use *Student Math Handbook* pages 65, 66, 68 for reference and review. See pages 145–152 in the back of this unit.

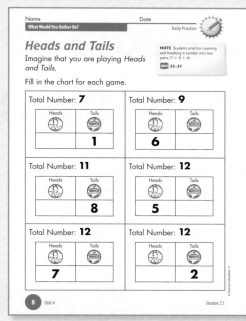

▲ **Student Activity Book, p. 8**

"Eagle or Whale?" Representations

Math Focus Points

◆ Making sense of data representations, including pictures, bar graphs, tallies, and Venn Diagrams

◆ Making a representation to communicate the results of a survey

◆ Comparing what different representations communicate about a set of data

Vocabulary

tally mark

Today's Plan		Materials
ACTIVITY ① *Quick Survey:* **Left-Handed or Right-Handed?**	🕐 10 MIN 👥 CLASS	• *Quick Survey* Chart: "Left-Handed or Right-Handed?"*
ACTIVITY ② **Representations of "Eagle or Whale?" Data,** *continued*	🕐 30 MIN 👤 INDIVIDUALS 👥 PAIRS	• Connecting cube representation of "Eagle or Whale?" data (from Session 2.1); students' "Eagle or Whale?" data representations (from Session 2.1); connecting cubes; stick-on dots; self-stick notes; crayons or markers; 12″ x 18″ paper; collections for *Guess My Rule* (optional)
DISCUSSION ③ **"Eagle or Whale?" Representations**	🕐 20 MIN 👥 CLASS	• Connecting cube representation of "Eagle or Whale?" data (from Session 2.1); students' "Eagle or Whale?" data representations
SESSION FOLLOW-UP ④ **Daily Practice**		• *Student Activity Book,* p. 9 • *Student Math Handbook,* pp. 65, 66, 67, 68

*See *Materials to Prepare,* p. 49.

Classroom Routines

Morning Meeting: Mixed-Up Calendar Follow your daily *Morning Meeting* Routine.
During *Calendar,* choose two cards for the days of the week and change their position on the calendar so that they are out of order. Ask students to find the mistakes and to help you fix them.

ACTIVITY

1 *Quick Survey:* Left-Handed or Right-Handed?

10 MIN   CLASS

Spend a few minutes reviewing or introducing tally marks❶ to students, as needed.

Sometimes when people record data from a survey, they use something called tally marks to help them count. When you use tally marks, you make one line for each person, but when you get to the 5th person you make a diagonal line across the group instead in order to show a group of five.

Demonstrate this on the board, counting up to 12 as you make the tally marks, emphasizing 5 and 10 when you make the diagonal lines.

People usually use tally marks because it can make it easier to count. I could count the tally marks I made by 1s: 1, 2, 3, 4, 5, 6, 7, 8, 9, 10, 11, 12.

1 2 3 4 5   6 7 8 9 10   11 12

Or I could count them by 5s and then count by 1s when there are no more 5s: 5, 10, 11, 12.

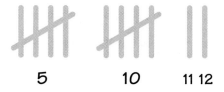

5   10   11 12

Teaching Note

❶ **Using Tally Marks** Students in Grade 1 have had some exposure to using tally marks to count. Use this opportunity to model the use of tally marks in collecting data. Students will vary in their abilities to use and understand tallies. In Grade 2, students work further with tallies as they begin to use groups to count.

Now do the following *Quick Survey* with your students.

Are you left-handed or right-handed?

Use tally marks to record the responses to the survey on the "Left-Handed or Right-Handed?" *Quick Survey* chart. After recording all of the responses, count them by 1s and then by 5s.

Are you left-handed or right-handed?

Left-Handed	Right-Handed
||||	✖✖✖ ✖✖✖ ✖✖✖ ✖✖ |

Afterward, have a short discussion about the results of the survey. Use questions such as the following to guide the discussion:

- What does this survey tell us about our class?

- How many people are left-handed? How many people are right-handed? Are there more people who are left-handed or right-handed?

- How many people answered the survey?

- Can you think of an equation that would show what we found out?

- Do you think we'd get similar data if we asked this question on a different day? What if we did the same survey in another class?

Keep the *Quick Survey* chart "Left-Handed or Right-Handed?" displayed in the room for students to refer to later.

ONGOING ASSESSMENT: Observing Students at Work

Students make sense of tally marks in a data representation.

- **Are students able to determine the number of responses in each category and the total number of responses by using the tally marks?**

- **Can students generate an equation that represents the data?**

ACTIVITY

2 Representations of "Eagle or Whale?" Data, *continued*

30 MIN INDIVIDUALS PAIRS

Students finish their representations of the "Eagle or Whale?" data begun in Session 2.1.

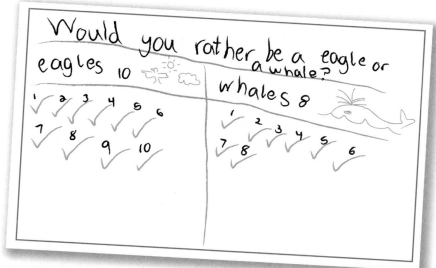

Sample Student Work

If students finish their representations, they can pair up and play *Guess My Rule* with one rule, using a collection they have not yet used, or they can play *Guess My Rule* with two rules. (See "Differentiation: Supporting the Range of Learners" in Session 1.4, page 42, for a description of *Guess My Rule* with two rules.)

ONGOING ASSESSMENT: Observing Students at Work

For Ongoing Assessment for this activity, see Session 2.1, page 57.

DISCUSSION

3 "Eagle or Whale?" Representations

20 MIN CLASS

Math Focus Points for Discussion

◆ Comparing what different representations communicate about a set of data

Math Note

② Variety of Representations Different representations will highlight different aspects of the data. For example:

- One representation may make it easier to see how many more students chose eagles than whales.
- Another representation may more clearly show that the data is about eagles and whales.
- Another representation may show the names of the students who wanted to be eagles and the names of the students who wanted to be whales.

Display the connecting cube representation of the "Eagle or Whale?" data from Session 2.1. Post students' representations so that everyone can see them, or ask students to hold up their representations.

Look at your classmates' representations. What do you notice is the same or similar in many of your representations?

Students may notice the following similarities:

- The representations are all about eagles and whales.
- In each, some liked eagles and some liked whales.
- Most or all representations show the same amount in each group.

How are your representations different?

Students may notice the following differences:

- Some students used pictures.
- Some students used lines to represent the data.
- Some students organized the data in groups.
- Some students made lists.

Choose one of the students' representations. Point out to students one thing that you can easily tell by looking at that student's representation.②

When I look at [Allie's] representation, I can easily tell that there were more people that wanted to be eagles than whales because she put a line of self-stick notes for the people who wanted to be eagles. Underneath, she put a line of self-stick notes for the people who wanted to be whales. I can easily see that there are more eagle self-stick notes than whale self-stick notes.

Choose a representation in which the student represented the data differently from the first student you discussed and ask students this question:

What can you tell easily from [Diego's] representation?

Look at two or three more representations in which students represented the data in different ways and ask the same question.

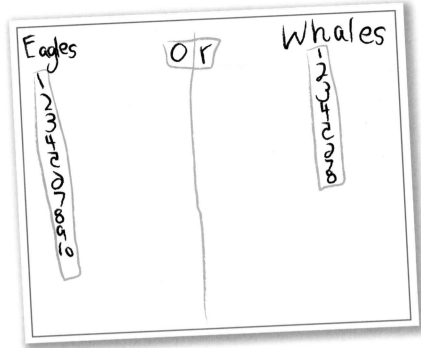

Sample Student Work

Sample Student Work

Eleven Shapes: How Many of Each?

I have 11 shapes.

Some are circles. ○

Some are triangles. △

How many of each could I have?

Solve the problem. Show your work.

Ongoing Review

There should be 8 crayons in the box.
How many more are needed?

Ⓐ   Ⓑ   Ⓒ   Ⓓ

▲ **Student Activity Book, p. 9**

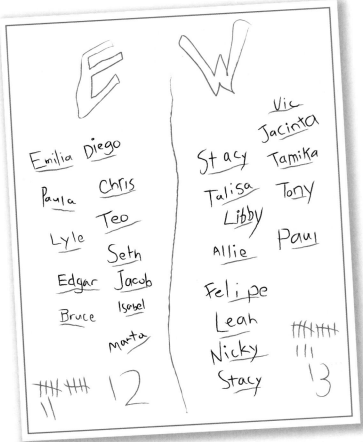

Sample Student Work

SESSION FOLLOW-UP

4 Daily Practice

Daily Practice: For ongoing review, have students complete *Student Activity Book* page 9.

Student Math Handbook: Students and families may use *Student Math Handbook* pages 65, 66, 67, 68 for reference and review. See pages 145–152 in the back of this unit.

Surveys

Math Focus Points

- ◈ Choosing a survey question
- ◈ Making a plan for gathering data
- ◈ Collecting and keeping track of survey data

Today's Plan		Materials
ACTIVITY **① Introducing Class Surveys: Choosing a Question**	15 MIN · CLASS · PAIRS	• *Student Activity Book,* p. 10 • Chart: "Choosing A Question"*
ACTIVITY **② Making a Plan**	15 MIN · CLASS · PAIRS	• *Student Activity Book,* p. 10 • T35, Our Plan for Collecting Data • Planning Charts*
ACTIVITY **③ Collecting Survey Data**	30 MIN · PAIRS	• Materials for collecting data, such as connecting cubes and self-stick notes; class list*; blank paper; clipboards (optional)
SESSION FOLLOW-UP **④ Daily Practice**		• *Student Activity Book,* p. 11 • *Student Math Handbook,* pp. 65, 66, 67, 68

*See *Materials to Prepare,* p. 49.

Classroom Routines

Start With/Get To: Forward or Backward? Choose both the *start with* and *get to* numbers from a basket holding the numbers 1 to 60. Ask students to find and mark both numbers on the number line. Decide as a class if you will be counting forward or backward (up or down). As a class, count from the *start with* number to the *get to* number.

Differentiation

① English Language Learners You may wish to meet with English Language Learners as a small group to help put their questions into standard English form before sharing them with the rest of the class.

15 MIN   CLASS   PAIRS

ACTIVITY

Introducing Class Surveys: Choosing a Question

Post the "Choosing a Question" chart you prepared ahead of time.

During the next two days you are going to do your own survey with our class. You are going to decide on a question that has only two possible responses. Then, you will ask your classmates your survey question and record their responses. Later, you will make a representation of what you found out.

Show students the "Choosing a Question" chart and emphasize that the type of questions on the chart have only two responses. Read through the different types of questions. Then, brainstorm questions that would fit under each type and record them.①

| Would you rather _____ or _____? |

Would you rather eat grapes or an apple?
Would you rather play in the snow or on the beach?

| Which do you like better _____ or _____? |

Which do you like better: spaghetti or pizza?
Which do you like better: winter or summer?

| Do you _____ or _____? |

Do you live in an apartment or a house?
Do you walk to school or ride the bus to school?

| Which is harder for you _____ or _____? |

Which is harder for you: skipping or tying your shoes?
Which is harder for you: swimming or riding a bike?

| Are you _____ or _____? |

Are you left-handed or right-handed?
Are you the oldest or not?

Organize students in pairs.❷ Then as a class, read the completed "Choosing a Question" chart, noting the question types and the class's examples of survey questions that reflect each type.

You and your partner are going to decide on a question to ask the rest of our class. Your question can have only two responses, but you can decide what your question will be.

Each pair should check with you after they have chosen their question so that you can make sure that it is a reasonable question with only two responses.

After you have checked their questions, have students record them on *Student Activity Book* page 10. They will fill out the rest of the page during the next activity.

ACTIVITY

❷ Making a Plan

15 MIN　CLASS　PAIRS

Bring students together to discuss how to make a plan for collecting their data.

After you have decided on and recorded your question, you will need to make a plan for how you are going to do your survey.

Display the transparency of Our Plan for Collecting Data (T35) on the overhead. Post the two planning charts, "How will you record students' responses?" and "How will you make sure that you asked everyone?" that you have prepared ahead of time.

For this demonstration of how to fill out *Student Activity Book* page 10, choose a survey question that has two possible responses to use as an example. Select a question that you do not think one of the pairs has chosen. With the class, fill out the first three questions on the transparency of Our Plan for Collecting Data (T35), using the example you have chosen.

Question 4 says: How will you record students' responses? What are some ways we could record the responses that students give to our survey, [the one you are using as an example]?

Show students the materials you have available for keeping track of responses. Brainstorm possible responses for Question 4 and record them on the chart. Then choose one suggestion and record it on the transparency of Our Plan for Collecting Data (T35).

Name _____ Date _____

What Would You Rather Be?

Our Plan for Collecting Data ✎

1. What is your question?

   _____

   _____

2. Who will ask the question?

   _____

3. Who will record students' responses?

   _____

4. How will you record students' responses?

   _____

   _____

5. How will you make sure that you asked everyone?

   _____

   _____

10　Unit 4　　　Session 2.3

▲ **Student Activity Book, p. 10;**
Transparencies, T35

> **How will you record students' answers?**
>
> - Use a check list, put a letter next to everyone's name.
>
> - Write names down, make a red dot for one answer and blue dot for another.
>
> - Get red cubes for one answer and blue cubes for the other.

Question 5 says, How will you make sure that you asked everyone? What are some ways we could make sure that we asked everyone our survey question?

Brainstorm possible responses for question 5, and record them on the chart. Choose one suggestion and record it on the transparency of Our Plan for Collecting Data (T35).

> **How will you make sure that you asked everyone?**
>
> - Count to make sure we got 21 answers.
>
> - Put an answer next to people's names on a class list.
>
> - Put a check next to everybody's name.

When it seems that everyone understands how to plan their survey, students should work with their partners to fill out *Student Activity Book* page 10.

Check in with pairs to make sure that they are thinking about and answering the questions on *Student Activity Book* page 10. You can do this by asking them questions about their plan. For some students it may be important to stress that they do not need to write long sentences in response to the questions.

1. What is your question?

WUD YOU bE A RAVIN oR ROBIN

2. Who will ask the question?

DANiellE

3. Who will record students' responses?

SeTh

4. How will you record students' responses?

I Will MAR A LIeADAON peS oFCopaper WATh TWo cotegories

5. How will you make sure that you asked everyone?

we will count 22 kids

Sample Student Work

1. What is your question?

Do you Like BoBcats or tigers

2. Who will ask the question?

Leah

3. Who will record students' responses?

Neal

4. How will you record students' responses?

a scrap pepc of papr and ask pepol

5. How will you make sure that you asked everyone?

we're affter going to cowt

Sample Student Work

ONGOING ASSESSMENT: Observing Students at Work

Students choose a survey question and plan how they will collect the responses to the survey.

- **Can students come up with a survey question that has only two possible responses?**

- **Do students think through how they are going to do their survey?** Can they choose an appropriate way to record the data they collect?

- **How do they make sure that everyone answers the survey?**

DIFFERENTIATION: Supporting the Range of Learners

Intervention Some students may need your help in making a plan. Consider selecting a recording method that you know will work well for them and help them get started by collecting a few responses together.

ACTIVITY

③ Collecting Survey Data

30 MIN   PAIRS

Have available the materials students can use for collecting the data, including blank paper and class lists.

For the remainder of the session, students collect responses to their survey. Choose a way to organize their collection of data that is comfortable for you. Here are three ways that some teachers have chosen to set up collecting data:

- All of the students collect their data at the same time during this activity.

- A few pairs collect their data during this activity while other students play *Guess My Rule* with one rule or with two rules. In this setup, the pairs collecting data ask their questions of students who are playing the games.

- Students collect their data throughout the day, a few pairs at a time.

Regardless of how you choose to have students collect data, they should be ready to make representations of that data during the next session.

Students can use tools such as connecting cubes or class lists to help keep track of the responses to their surveys.

As students collect their data, some problems may come up. For example, they may lose track of whom they have asked and whom they have not asked, or they may need to deal with unanticipated responses. It is important that students have the opportunity to work on these difficulties themselves, but you may need to facilitate their problem solving. Asking students questions about what they might do will help them in this process. For example, you might ask the following:

• How can you figure out whom you didn't ask?

• How could you use a class list to help you?

• [Lyle] had a different answer from the choices you gave him. How might you record his answer?

ONGOING ASSESSMENT: Observing Students at Work

Students collect and record data from their own survey question.

• **Do students understand the question they are asking and can they explain it to others?**

• **Are students collecting data systematically from every member of the class?**

• **How are students keeping track of who has responded and who has not?**

• **How do students identify and solve "messy data" problems?** How do they deal with missing students or students who give unanticipated responses?

Name _____ Date _____

What Would You Rather Be?   Daily Practice

Monthly Calendar

Here is a calendar for you. Fill in the
month and dates. Then, find a place
to hang it at home.

NOTE Students practice
recording dates and making,
reading, and using a calendar as
a tool for keeping track of time.
SMH 17–18

_____

Name of Month

Sunday	Monday	Tuesday	Wednesday	Thursday	Friday	Saturday

Special Days

_____   _____
_____   _____

Session 2.3   Unit 4 **11**

▲ **Student Activity Book, p. 11**

SESSION FOLLOW-UP
4 Daily Practice

Daily Practice: For ongoing review, have students complete
Student Activity Book page 11.

Student Math Handbook: Students and families may use
Student Math Handbook pages 65, 66, 67, 68 for reference and
review. See pages 145–152 in the back of this unit.

Representing Survey Data

Math Focus Points

◆ Collecting and keeping track of survey data

◆ Interpreting the results of a data investigation

Today's Plan		Materials
DISCUSSION **① Collecting Survey Data**	10 MIN CLASS	• Students' survey data (from Session 2.3)
ACTIVITY **② Representing Survey Data**	45 MIN PAIRS	• *Student Activity Book,* p. 12 • Students' survey data (from Session 2.3); 12″ x 18″ paper; markers or crayons; self-stick notes, stick-on dots, and other materials to make representations; class lists (from Session 2.3)
ACTIVITY **③ Collecting Data for the Assessment**	5 MIN CLASS	• Class list
SESSION FOLLOW-UP **④ Daily Practice and Homework**		• *Student Activity Book,* pp. 12–14 • *Student Math Handbook,* pp. 66, 68

Classroom Routines

Quick Images: Coins Using the set of overhead coins, display 3 pennies, 2 nickels, and 1 quarter. Follow the basic *Quick Images* activity. Discuss the quantity and type of coins with the class. Ask questions that focus on identifying each coin and the total number of coins (e.g., Which coin is the [quarter]? What is the name of *this* coin? How many [pennies] did you see? Which coin is not shown?). If time permits, repeat using 3 dimes and 2 pennies.

DISCUSSION

1 Collecting Survey Data

10 MIN   CLASS

Math Focus Points for Discussion

◆ Collecting and keeping track of survey data

Hold a brief discussion with students about the process of collecting survey data. Students bring their recordings of their classmates' responses with them to this discussion.

Students share methods for collecting survey data.

Ask the following questions to guide the discussion:

* What method of recording your classmates' responses worked best for you?

* How did you make sure that you had asked everyone?

* What was difficult about collecting responses to your survey?

* How did you solve any problems you had?

ACTIVITY

2 Representing Survey Data

45 MIN   PAIRS

Today, you are going to make a representation of the responses you got to your survey, as you did for the "Eagle or Whale?" question. Can someone remind us what a representation is?

If no one is sure, you can remind students that a representation is a way to show what you found out from a survey. Also refer to the various *Quick Survey* charts posted around the room.

You might represent your data in a way that is similar to how you represented the "Eagle or Whale?" data, or you might try showing your data in a different way. What are some ways you could show your data?

Encourage students to share a variety of ways to represent their data. If students bring up writing a sentence or using words as a way of representing their data, ask that they use pictures or other material in addition to writing a sentence. Representing a set of data visually, in addition to describing it with words, allows those looking at the representation to gather more information.

Whatever you decide to do for your representation, be sure to show what you found out clearly so that someone not in this class can understand what questions you asked and what you found out.❶ Make sure that you write your question on your representations.

Students work in pairs on their representations. They can choose which materials they want to use from the ones you provide.❷

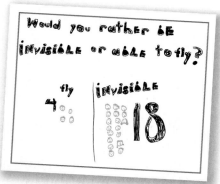

Sample Student Work   *Sample Student Work*

As students work, circulate to observe what they are doing and to help them focus on using their representations to communicate the results of their surveys. Ask questions such as these:

- What did you find out from your survey? What were the results of your survey?

- How are you thinking about showing your results on your paper?

Teaching Note

❶ **Real Audiences** If students share their representations with a real audience from outside the class, they will gain a clearer understanding of the purpose and importance of representations. You might invite parents or students from another class to come see the representations of their survey data. Alternatively, post the representations in the hallway for other people in your school to look at and learn about the surveys students did and the results.

Professional Development

❷ **Teacher Note:** Grade 1 Students' Representations of Data, p. 119

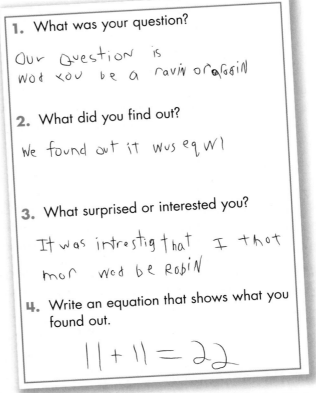

Name _____ Date _____

What Would You Rather Be?

What We Found Out ✎

1. What was your question?
   _____
   _____
   _____

2. What did you find out?
   _____
   _____
   _____

3. What surprised or interested you?
   _____
   _____
   _____

4. Write an equation that shows what you found out.
   _____
   _____
   _____

12 Unit 4   Sessions 2.4, 2.5

▲ Student Activity Book, p. 12 [PORTFOLIO] [WRITING]

- If I were not in our class and wanted to learn what you found out, would your representation show me that?

- What can I learn from your representation?

1. **What was your question?**

   Our Question is wot xou be a ravin or robin

2. **What did you find out?**

   We found out it wus eq wl

3. **What surprised or interested you?**

   It was intrestig that I thot mor wod be RobiN

4. **Write an equation that shows what you found out.**

   $11 + 11 = 22$

Sample Student Work

When students finish their representations, they should complete *Student Activity Book* page 12, which asks them to describe and interpret their data. Read through the questions together or with students as they finish their representations.

ONGOING ASSESSMENT: Observing Students at Work

Students organize and represent the results to their surveys.

- **Are students grouping data that belongs together?** Are their groups clear?

- **Do students' representations communicate the findings of the survey clearly?** What aspects are clear? What aspects need further clarification?

- **How accurately are students counting the survey data in each category?** Do they account for all the data in their representation?

DIFFERENTIATION: Supporting the Range of Learners

Intervention Some students may need support in getting started on their representations. They may still be unsure of what it means to represent a set of data. To help them get started, you can ask questions such as these:

- What did you find out when you did your survey?

- How could you show how many people [like vanilla ice cream] and how many people [don't like vanilla ice cream]?

- How could you show someone not in this class what you found out in your survey?

Some students may benefit from creating a very concrete representation. Suggest that they represent the data with connecting cubes. This will allow them to see each individual response as well as the responses as a group and physically move around the cubes that represent the responses.

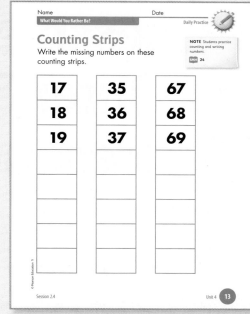
▲ Student Activity Book, p. 13

ACTIVITY

5 MIN **CLASS**

③ Collecting Data for the Assessment

In preparation for the assessment in the next session, gather the following data from your class. Ask students, "Would you rather explore the deep sea or outer space?" *Do not* represent or discuss the data as a group. Instead, record the data yourself on a class list. Tell students that they will work tomorrow on organizing and representing these data themselves.

SESSION FOLLOW-UP

④ Daily Practice and Homework

 Daily Practice: For ongoing review, have students complete *Student Activity Book* page 13.

 Homework: Students analyze and organize the results of a survey on *Student Activity Book* page 14.

 Student Math Handbook: Students and families may use *Student Math Handbook* pages 66, 68 for reference and review. See pages 145–152 in the back of this unit.

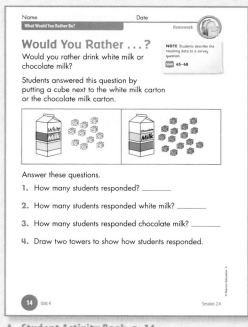
▲ Student Activity Book, p. 14

Assessment: "Deep Sea or Outer Space?" Representations

Math Focus Points

◆ Describing and comparing the number of pieces of data in each category or at each value and interpreting what the data tell you about the group surveyed

◆ Interpreting results of a data investigation

◆ Making a representation to communicate the results of a survey

Today's Plan		Materials
DISCUSSION **① Sharing Survey Results**	30 MIN CLASS	• Completed *Student Activity Book,* p. 12 (from Session 2.4) • Students' survey representations (from Session 2.4)
ASSESSMENT ACTIVITY **② Assessment: "Deep Sea or Outer Space?" Representations**	✓ 30 MIN INDIVIDUALS	• M11* • Class lists with "Deep Sea or Outer Space?" data*
SESSION FOLLOW-UP **③ Daily Practice**		• *Student Activity Book,* p. 15 • *Student Math Handbook,* pp. 66, 68

*See *Materials to Prepare,* p. 51.

Classroom Routines

Start With/Get To: Counting Forward Divide the *Start With/Get To* cards between two baskets labeled *start with* (cards 1–30) and *get to* (cards 31–60). Choose a *start with* number from the first basket and a *get to* number from the second. For this variation, ask students to find and mark both numbers on the 100 chart. As a class, count from the *start with* number to the *get to* number.

DISCUSSION
Sharing Survey Results

30 MIN   CLASS

Professional Development
❶ **Dialogue Box:** Sharing Survey Findings, p. 141

Math Focus Points for Discussion

◆ Describing and comparing the number of pieces of data in each category or at each value and interpreting what the data tell you about the group

◆ Interpreting results of a data investigation

Pairs of students share their representations and findings with the class. Students should bring their representations with them and can use their completed *Student Activity Book* page 12 as a prompt.

> You are now going to have a chance to share your survey with all of us. When you share your survey, please tell us the question you asked, show us your representation, tell us what you found out from your survey, and tell us anything that surprised or interested you.

As students share their surveys, you may need to ask them some questions to bring out what they learned.❶

If you do not have time for everyone to share in this 30-minute discussion, plan to continue another day. ❷

Consider posting students' work in the classroom or hallway, as a way of sharing their survey results with a larger audience.

Teaching Note

❷ **Allocating Time** Because students will need 30 minutes to complete the assessment activity, limit their discussion to 30 minutes.

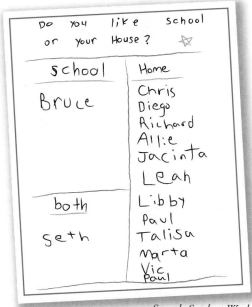

Sample Student Work

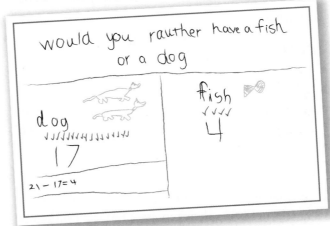

Sample Student Work

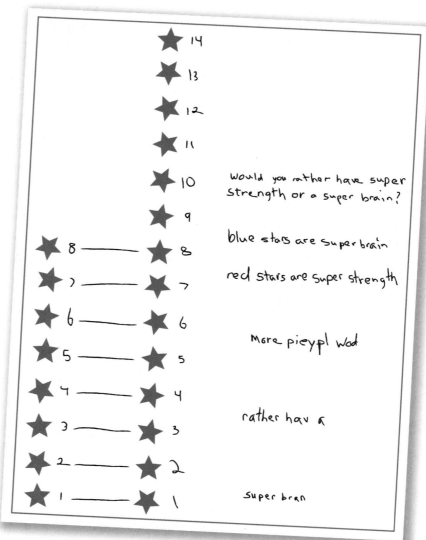

Sample Student Work

ASSESSMENT ACTIVITY

2 Assessment: "Deep Sea or Outer Space?" Representations

30 MIN INDIVIDUALS

This assessment focuses on Benchmark 2: Represent a set of data with two categories and Benchmark 3: Interpret a variety of data representations with two categories.

Each student will need Assessment: "Deep Sea or Outer Space?" Representations (M11) and a copy of the class list on which you recorded the data you collected from the survey question: "Would you rather explore the deep sea or outer space?"

Here is a class list with the data we collected yesterday about whether you would rather explore the deep sea or outer space. You are going to make representations of these data on a sheet of paper. Make sure that you show clearly what we found out so that someone who is not in this class can understand it. When you have finished making a representation, you are going to answer some questions about what you found out.

ONGOING ASSESSMENT: Observing Students at Work

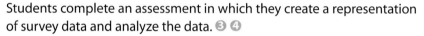

Students complete an assessment in which they create a representation of survey data and analyze the data. ❸ ❹

- **Do students create representations that accurately represent the set of data?** Do their representations clearly communicate what the data show?

- **How do students represent the data?** Do they use pictures? Do they include numbers?

- **Are students' categories visually distinctive?**

- **Can students use their representations to describe what they found out?** Do they refer to what the data tells them about the people surveyed?

Teaching Note

❸ **Assessment: "Deep Sea or Outer Space?"** Students create a representation of data collected from their class and write about what they found out from their survey (Benchmarks 2 and 3).

Professional Development

❹ **Teacher Note:** Assessment: Deep Sea or Outer Space? Representations, p. 124

Name _____ Date _____
What Would You Rather Be?

Assessment: "Deep Sea or Outer Space?" Representations

1. On a separate sheet of paper, make a representation of the data we collected from this question: Would you rather explore the deep sea or outer space?

Then answer these questions:

2. What did you find out from this survey?
_____
_____
_____

3. What surprised or interested you?
_____
_____
_____
_____

Session 2.5   Unit 4 M11

▲ **Resource Masters, M11** PORTFOLIO

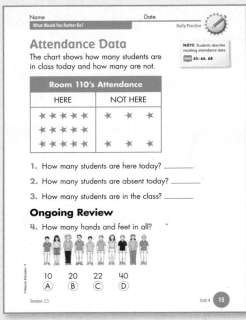

▲ Student Activity Book, p. 15

SESSION FOLLOW-UP

3 Daily Practice

 Daily Practice: For reinforcment of this unit's content, have students complete *Student Activity Book* page 15.

Student Math Handbook: Students and families may use *Student Math Handbook* pages 66, 68 for reference and review. See pages 145–147 in the back of this unit.

Mathematical Emphases

Data Analysis Sorting and classifying

Math Focus Points

◆ Using attributes to sort a set of objects

Data Analysis Representing data

Math Focus Points

◆ Making a representation to communicate the results of a survey

◆ Making sense of data representations, including pictures, bar graphs, tallies, and Venn diagrams

◆ Comparing what different representations communicate about a set of data

◆ Organizing data in numerical order

Data Analysis Describing data

Math Focus Points

◆ Describing and comparing the number of pieces of data in each category or at each value and interpreting what the data tell you about the group

◆ Using data to compare how two groups are similar or different

◆ Understanding that the sum of the pieces of data in all the categories equals the number of people surveyed

Comparing Age Data

	Student Activity Book	Student Math Handbook	Professional Development: Read Ahead of Time	
SESSION 3.1 p. 90				
How Old Are We? Students represent their ages with connecting cubes and figure out how many students are each age. They create their own representations of this age data.	16	65, 66, 67, 68	• **Teacher Note:** Grade 1 Students' Representations of Data, p. 119	
SESSION 3.2 p. 98				
Ages of Another Class Students discuss and compare representations that they made of their class's age data, and then make representations of age data from another Grade 1 class.	17–18	65, 66, 67, 68		

Morning Meeting
- No materials needed

Start With/Get To
- *Start with/Get to* cards 1–60
- Two baskets
- Class 100 chart

Quick Images
- Set of overhead coins

Materials to Gather	Materials to Prepare
• **12" x 18" paper** (one per pair, plus extras) • **Markers or crayons** (as needed) • **Self-stick notes, stick-on dots, connecting cubes, color tiles, and other materials to make representations** (as needed) • **Chart paper** (optional)	• *Quick Survey* **Chart: "Child or Grown Up?"** Write the title "Would you rather be a child or a grown-up?" on a piece of chart paper. Create a bar graph and number it to 15 or 20 as shown on page 91. Label one column "Child" and one column "Grown-up." See completed chart on page 91.
	• *Quick Survey* **Chart** Choose a question that relates to your classroom or your school, preferably one that will help you or someone else make a decision. Title a sheet of chart paper with the question you have selected. Make a table with one column labeled with one of the responses to the question you selected and the other column labeled with the other response. See the Teaching Note on page 99 for suggestions. • **Student Work for Representation Discussion** Select three or four of students' representations of ages from Session 3.1 to show and discuss. You may choose to draw some representations on chart paper yourself, or you can have the students' representations ready to show to the class. (See pages 101 and 102 for suggestions about what types of examples to choose.) • **M12, Ages from a Grade 1 Class** Make copies or choose the alternative below. (one per pair) • **Age Data** As an alternative to using the Resource Master listed above, collect age data from another Grade 1 class at your school. Record the data on a class list and make one copy for each student. (1 per pair; optional)

Comparing Age Data,
continued

SESSION 3.3 p. 104	Student Activity Book	Student Math Handbook	Professional Development: Read Ahead of Time	
Comparing Age Data Students use representations to compare the ages of another Grade 1 class with the ages of the students in their own class. Then they make a chart showing their ages and the ages of their siblings and discuss what they can find out from this data display.	19–21	65, 66, 67, 68	• **Teacher Note:** Describing Data, p. 122 • **Dialogue Box:** Us and Our Siblings, p. 143	
SESSION 3.4 p. 110				
End-of-Unit Assessment Students complete three assessment problems. In one, they decide on a rule by which they sort a set of buttons. In the other two, they read representations of sets of data and describe the data in those representations.	23	65, 66, 67, 68	• **Teacher Note:** End-of-Unit Assessment, p. 129 • **Assessment in This Unit,** p. 14	

Materials to Gather	Materials to Prepare
• **M12, Ages from a Grade 1 Class** (from Session 3.2) • **Students' representations of ages** (from Session 3.1) • **Self-stick notes in two colors** (as needed) • **Markers** (one per student)	• **Chart: "Us and Our Siblings"** Tape two sheets of chart paper together vertically for this chart. Write the title "Us and Our Siblings" on the top of the chart paper.
	• **M13–M15, End-of-Unit Assessment** Make copies. (1 per student) • *Quick Survey* **Chart: "Curly Hair or Straight Hair?"** Title a sheet of chart paper on the long side "Is your hair curly or straight?" Make a Venn diagram by drawing two overlapping circles, one labeled "Curly Hair" and one labeled "Straight Hair." See page 111 for an example.

How Old Are We?

Math Focus Points

◆ Making sense of data representations, including pictures, bar graphs, tallies, and Venn diagrams

◆ Making a representation to communicate the results of a survey

◆ Organizing data in numerical order

◆ Describing and comparing the number of pieces of data in each category or at each value and interpreting what the data tell you about the group

Today's Plan			Materials
1 ACTIVITY *Quick Survey:* **Child or Grown-Up?**	🕐 10 MIN	👥 CLASS	• *Quick Survey* Chart: "Child or Grown Up?"*
2 ACTIVITY How Old Are We?	🕐 20 MIN	👥 CLASS	• Connecting cubes (as needed)
3 ACTIVITY Representations of Our Ages	🕐 30 MIN	👥 PAIRS	• 12″ x 18″ paper; grid paper (as needed); markers or crayons (as needed); self-stick notes, stick-on dots, connecting cubes, color tiles, and other materials to make representations (as needed); chart paper (optional)
4 SESSION FOLLOW-UP Daily Practice			• *Student Activity Book,* p. 16 • *Student Math Handbook,* pp. 65, 66, 67, 68

*See *Materials to Prepare,* p. 87.

Classroom Routines

Start With/Get To: Counting Forward Choose the *start with* number from the first basket (cards 1–30) and the *get to* number from the second (cards 31–60). Ask students to find and mark both numbers on the 100 chart. As a class, count from the *start with* number to the *get to* number.

ACTIVITY

1 *Quick Survey:* Child or Grown-Up?

10 MIN   CLASS

Post the "Child or Grown-Up?" *Quick Survey* chart that you have prepared.

Would you rather be a child or a grown-up?

Would you rather be a child or a grown-up?

Record students' responses and then have a short discussion about the representation and results of the survey. Use questions such as the following to guide the discussion:

- I used a bar graph to represent this data. What can you easily tell from looking at this representation? What is hard to tell from looking at this representation?

- What does this survey tell us about our class?

- How many people would rather be a child? How many people would rather be a grown-up? Would more people rather be a child or a grown-up? Would very many more people rather be [a child] or just a few more? How many more?

- How many people answered this survey? What is an equation that can show the results of this survey?

- Why do you think more people would rather be [a grown-up]?

- Do you think we'd get similar data if we asked adults the same question?

Teaching Note

① *Quick Survey* Read the *Quick Survey* activity in Session 1.1 (page 23) for information on how to structure the surveys, the purpose of these surveys, and suggestions for choosing survey questions.

ONGOING ASSESSMENT: Observing Students at Work

Students respond to a survey question, and then describe and discuss the data which is represented in a bar graph.

- **Are students able to describe and compare the data in different ways?**

- **Are students able to identify the number of people who answered the survey?** Can they give an equation that describes the data?

ACTIVITY

How Old Are We?

20 MIN   CLASS

Today we are going to talk about all of the different ages of the children in our class. What do you think is the youngest age of someone in this class? What would the oldest age probably be?

Take students' suggestions and write a list of possible ages on the board.

5   6   7   8

We are going to show how old children are in this class by using connecting cubes. I would like you to build a tower with connecting cubes to show how old you are. For example, if you are 6 years old, your cube tower should have 6 connecting cubes in it.

After students have built connecting cube towers for their ages, ask the youngest age group in the class to line up their towers on a table or along the white board tray. Do the same with each successive age group.

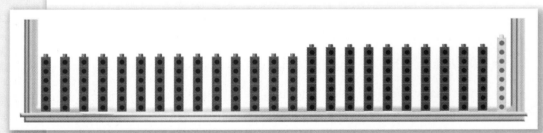

Let's look at this line of connecting cube towers. What can we tell about the ages of the students in our class?

Students are likely to notice how many students are at each age level. Someone may notice that you can tell how many students there are in class by counting all the towers.

Count the number of towers for each age and then record the amounts on the board.

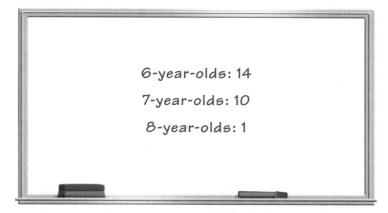

6-year-olds: 14

7-year-olds: 10

8-year-olds: 1

From how many students did we collect data? How do you know?

Can someone think of an equation we could write that shows how many students are each age and from how many students we collected data?

Write the equations students come up with on the board as shown.

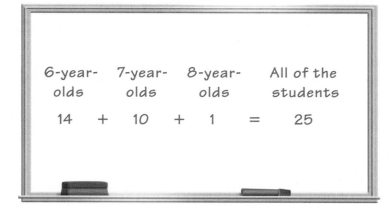

6-year-olds		7-year-olds		8-year-olds		All of the students
14	+	10	+	1	=	25

End the discussion by asking students to predict how the ages in another Grade 1 class might be similar or different.

ACTIVITY

③ Representations of Our Ages

30 MIN PAIRS

Now you are going to work with a partner to make your own representation of what we found out about how old the students are in our class. Suppose that someone came into our class and you wanted to show that person how old people are in our class.

To make your representation, you can use whatever materials you want: connecting cubes, stick-on dots, self-stick notes, blank paper, or grid paper. Whatever materials you choose to use, your representation should show clearly what we found out about how old students are in our class.

Distribute blank paper to each pair of students.

If students seem unsure of what to do, you might go through the different materials and ask how each material could be used to make a representation. Suggest that if students use connecting cubes, they should use them in a different way than you did as a whole group. Encourage students to make representations that make sense to them.❷❸

After students have finished, select three or four of their representations to show and discuss during Session 3.2. Select at least three different kinds of representations. You might include, for example, the following representations:

- One that includes student names

- One that includes a depiction of each age (e.g., rows of 6 stick-on dots and rows of 7 stick-on dots)

- A chart with each piece of data represented by a symbol (e.g., a checkmark or a star)

- A bar graph

Sample Student Work

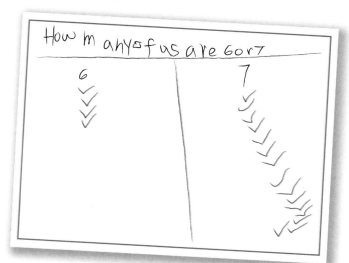

Sample Student Work

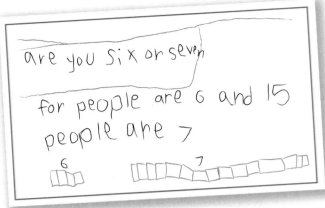

Sample Student Work

You may choose certain representations and draw them on chart paper yourself so that they are not particularly connected to any one child, or you can just have the children's representations ready to show to the class.

ONGOING ASSESSMENT: Observing Students at Work

As students create representations of data collected from the class, they are working on communicating and organizing data.

- **Do students keep track of the data they are representing?** Do they check to see whether all data is represented?

- **How have students chosen to represent the data?** Do they show each individual age in a way similar to the age tower, or do they use one cube or square to represent one person's data?

- **Do they group and/or order their data?** If so, how?

- **Can you tell by looking at their representation what it is about?**

- **Are students grouping the data that belong together?** Are their categories distinct?

DIFFERENTIATION: Supporting the Range of Learners

Intervention Some students may be confused about which quantity they are supposed to represent. In this survey, there are two quantities: the ages, and the number of students who are that age. If students represent only the ages, such as six or seven years, and not the number of students who are that age, ask the following questions:

- What could I find out about the ages of students in this class from looking at your representation?

- How many students are six? How many are seven?

- How could you show how many students are six and how many are seven?

SESSION FOLLOW-UP
4 Daily Practice

 Daily Practice: For ongoing review, have students complete *Student Activity Book* page 16.

 Student Math Handbook: Students and families may use *Student Math Handbook* pages 65, 66, 67, 68 for reference and review. See pages 145–152 in the back of this unit.

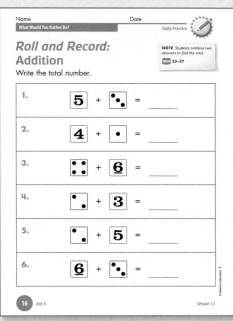

▲ Student Activity Book, p. 16

Ages of Another Class

Math Focus Points

◆ Making a representation to communicate the results of a survey

◆ Comparing what different representations communicate about a set of data

◆ Organizing data in numerical order

Today's Plan		Materials
ACTIVITY **①** *Quick Survey:* **About Your Class**	10 MIN CLASS	• *Quick Survey* Chart: "About Your Class"*
DISCUSSION **②** **Representations of Our Ages**	20 MIN CLASS	• Three or four of students' representations of ages or teacher-drawn copies of representations (from Session 3.1)*
ACTIVITY **③** **Ages of Another Class**	30 MIN PAIRS	• M12 or a set of age data from another Grade 1 class (optional)*
SESSION FOLLOW-UP **④** **Daily Practice and Homework**		• *Student Activity Book,* pp. 17–18 • *Student Math Handbook,* pp. 65, 66, 67, 68

*See *Materials to Prepare,* p. 87.

Classroom Routines

Quick Images: Coins   Using the set of overhead coins, display 3 nickels and 2 quarters. Follow the basic *Quick Images* activity. Discuss the quantity and type of coins with the class. Ask questions that focus on identifying each coin and the total number of coins (e.g., What is the name of *this* coin? How are these coins similar? How are they different? How many [nickels] did you see? How do you know?). If time permits, repeat using 1 penny and 4 dimes.

ACTIVITY

Quick Survey: About Your Class

10 MIN CLASS

Pose the question that you have chosen and presented on the chart.❶

Record students' responses using tally marks.

> **What color should the school paint the hallway?**
>
> | red | blue |
> |-----|------|
> | 卌 ||| | 卌 卌 卌 | |

After recording students' responses, have a short discussion about the representation and the results of the survey. Use questions such as the following to guide the discussion:

- What does this survey tell us about our class?

- I used tally marks to represent this data. What is easy to tell from this representation? What is hard to tell?

- How many people [chose red]? How many people [chose blue]? How many more people [chose red] than [chose blue]?

- How many people answered this survey? What is an equation that can show the results of this survey?

- How could collecting this data help [the school]?

- How might the data be different if we asked another class the same question?

ONGOING ASSESSMENT: Observing Students at Work

- **Are students able to determine the number of responses in each category and the total number of responses by using the tally marks?**

- **Can students generate an equation that represents the data?**

- **Are they able to identify how the data might be helpful or useful?**

Teaching Note

❶ *Quick Survey* **Relevant to Your Class** Choose a question that relates to your classroom or school, preferably one that will help you or someone else make a decision. Some suggestions are:

- Which book would you prefer to read today: _____ or _____?
- Have you brought in your permission slips?
- Will you get a school lunch today?
- At recess do you usually play [on the jungle gym] or [on the blacktop]?
- Do you think the school should paint the hallway red or blue?

See Materials to Prepare, page 87, for more details.

DISCUSSION

Representations of Our Ages

20 MIN   CLASS

Math Focus Points for Discussion

◆ Comparing what different representations communicate about a set of data

Post the chart paper on which you drew three or four students' representations, or post the representations that you chose from Session 3.1.

Here are some different ways that students in our class represented the data about the ages of students in our class. Look at them carefully and then we will discuss the different ways you represented this data.

Choose one representation to begin with.

• How did this person represent our age data? Can you describe this person's representation?

• What is easy to tell by looking at this representation?

If students are not sure how to answer, you might give examples, such as these:

• I can easily see in this representation that there are more [7-year-olds] than [6-year-olds].

• I can easily see in this representation how old each student is because the person drew towers of six cubes and seven cubes.

You might ask students to find the representation in which it is easy to find specific information.

In which representation can you easily see who is six and who is seven?

After discussing what you can find out from a particular representation, ask students whether anyone made a similar representation to the one you have just discussed.

Go through each of the representations in a similar way.

ACTIVITY
Ages of Another Class

30 MIN PAIRS

In the last session you made some predictions about how you thought the ages in another Grade 1 class would be similar or different. I have collected data about the ages of students in another Grade 1 class [in this school].

Hand out the copies of Ages from a Grade 1 Class (M12) or the data set you collected. Read through the data together.

You are going to make a representation of the ages of students in another Grade 1 class. Just as when you made a representation of the ages of the students in our class, you can choose how to represent the ages in this class. Whatever way you choose to represent the ages, you need to show clearly what the ages are in this class. You might choose to do it the same way you did last time, or you might try a different way.

Sample Student Work

Name _____ Date _____

What Would You Rather Be?

Ages from a Grade 1 Class

Allie	6 years old
Bruce	6 years old
Carol	7 years old
Diego	6 years old
Emilia	7 years old
Felipe	6 years old
Isabel	8 years old
Jacinta	7 years old
Jacob	6 years old
Nicky	7 years old
Leah	6 years old
Lyle	6 years old
Libby	8 years old
Marta	7 years old
Paul	7 years old
Paula	7 years old
Seth	7 years old
Tamika	6 years old
Teo	7 years old

M12 Unit 4   Sessions 3.2, 3.3

© Pearson Education 1

▲ **Resource Masters, M12**

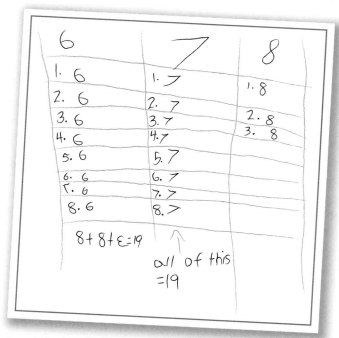

Sample Student Work

ONGOING ASSESSMENT: Observing Students at Work

As students create representations of data collected from another class, they work on communicating and organizing numerical data.

- **Do students keep track of the data they are representing?** Do they check to see whether everyone's data is represented?

- **How have students chosen to represent the data?** Do they show each individual age in a way similar to the age towers, or do they use one cube or square to represent one person's data?

- **Do students group and/or order their data?** If so, how?

- **Can you tell what students' representations are about by looking at them?**

- **Are students grouping the data that belong together?** Are their categories distinct?

- **How do students' representations of their class's age data compare with their representations of the other class's ages?** Did they represent the data in the same way? Did they try a different type of representation?

DIFFERENTIATION: Supporting the Range of Learners

Intervention Some students may find it challenging to consider a set of data that is not about them or that they did not collect. It is important to emphasize that these data from another class are different from those of their own class. In the next session, students will compare these two sets of data, which may also help them make better sense of data from outside their class. You may point out this comparison in the following way, if a student is having difficulty making sense of this set of data:

The ages of the students in this other class are different from the ages in our class. Do you see any ways that the ages are different?

It may also help students to have the opportunity to collect age data themselves from other classes.

SESSION FOLLOW-UP

Daily Practice and Homework

 Daily Practice: For ongoing review, have students complete *Student Activity Book,* page 17.

 Homework: Students collect age data for their family members on *Student Activity Book* page 18. Emphasize that they should bring their data to the next class session. Go over the example explaining how to record family members' ages. Students will need their homework in order to proceed with Session 3.3. Prepare a back-up plan for students who forget, such as asking them to fill in another sheet, listing the ages they know or estimating any they do not know.

 Student Math Handbook: Students and families may use *Student Math Handbook* pages 65, 66, 67, 68 for reference and review. See pages 145–152 in the back of this unit.

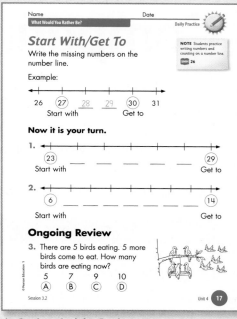

▲ Student Activity Book, p. 17

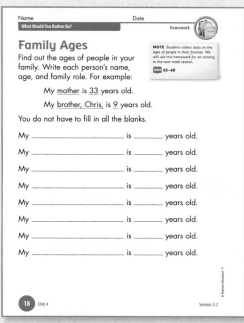

▲ Student Activity Book, p. 18

Comparing Age Data

Math Focus Points

◆ Using data to compare how two groups are similar or different

◆ Describing and comparing the number of pieces of data in each category or at each value and interpreting what the data tell you about the group

◆ Organizing data in numerical order

Vocabulary

compare

Today's Plan			Materials
ACTIVITY **1** *Quick Survey:* **What Color Are Your Shoes?**	10 MIN	CLASS	
ACTIVITY **2** **Comparing Classes**	20 MIN	PAIRS	• *Student Activity Book*, p. 19 • M12 • Students' representations of ages (from Session 3.1)
ACTIVITY **3** **Us and Our Siblings**	30 MIN	CLASS	• Completed *Student Activity Book*, p. 18 (from Session 3.2) • Chart: "Us and Our Siblings"*; self-stick notes in two colors (as needed); markers (one per student)
SESSION FOLLOW-UP **4** **Daily Practice and Homework**			• *Student Activity Book*, pp. 20–21 • *Student Math Handbook*, pp. 65, 66, 67, 68

*See *Materials to Prepare,* p. 89.

Classroom Routines

Start With/Get To: Counting Forward Choose the *start with* number from the first basket (cards 1–30) and the *get to* number from the second (cards 31-60). Ask students to find and mark both numbers on the 100 chart. After counting aloud as a class, have students write the numbers from the *start with* number to the *get to* number.

ACTIVITY

1 *Quick Survey:* What Color Are Your Shoes?

10 MIN | CLASS

What color are your shoes?

Make a physical graph with the students' shoes or have students stand in groups according to their shoe color. You will have to decide together what to do with shoes that are more than one color.

A class collects data about shoe color by physically organizing students in groups according to shoe color.

After organizing students or their shoes into groups, have a short discussion about the results of the survey. Use questions such as the following to guide the discussion:

- What does this survey tell us about our class?

- How many people's shoes are each color? [Record the number of each color.]

- How many people answered the survey?

- What is an equation that can show this data?

- What color shoes do many people have?

- What color shoes do not many people have?

Students respond to a survey question and describe and discuss the data.

- **What type of observations and comments do students make about the data?**

- **Are they able to count the number of responses and total the number of data?**

Teaching Note

❶ Comparing Data Because this is the first time students are asked to compare two sets of data, they may be unsure about how to make a comparison of the ages in each class. To help students, you might ask them to describe what they notice about the ages in the other class and then ask them to compare what they notice with their own class. For example, if a student states that there are more 6-year-olds than 7-year-olds in the other class, ask this question: Are there more 6-year-olds than 7-year-olds in our class?

Professional Development

❷ Teacher Note: Describing Data, p. 122

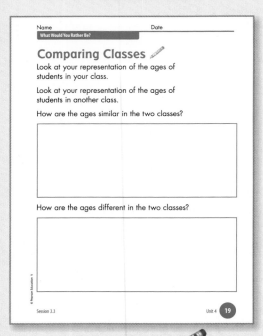

Name _____ Date _____

What Would You Rather Be?

Comparing Classes

Look at your representation of the ages of students in your class.

Look at your representation of the ages of students in another class.

How are the ages similar in the two classes?

How are the ages different in the two classes?

Session 3.3   Unit 4 **19**

▲ **Student Activity Book, p. 19** WRITING

ACTIVITY

❷ Comparing Classes

20 MIN   PAIRS

You are going to work with a partner to compare the ages of students in our class with the ages of students in the other class. Look together at both of your representations and think about what is similar about the ages in the two classes and what is different. Then answer the questions on *Student Activity Book* page 19.❶

After most students have answered both questions, bring the group together and ask them to share what they notice about the ages of the two classes.❷

ONGOING ASSESSMENT: Observing Students at Work

Students compare the ages of students in two Grade 1 classes, using the representations they created.

- **Are students able to read and gather information from their representations?**

- **Can students make statements about how the ages in the two classes are similar and different?**

- **Do they compare the classes?** Do they state which class has more 6-, 7-, or 8-year-olds? Do they notice that both classes have 6- and 7-year-olds?

ACTIVITY
③ Us and Our Siblings

30 MIN CLASS

Post the "Us and Our Siblings" chart you have prepared.

Students need to have completed *Student Activity Book* page 18 for this activity. Begin by having students share some of the ages of their family members. You might determine who is the oldest family member and who is the youngest family member in the class lists.

Today we are going to make a chart showing the ages of each of you in this class and the ages of all of your siblings.❸ Does anyone know what the word *"sibling"* means?

If no one knows the word, tell students that siblings are brothers and sisters.

We are going to put the data about our ages and our siblings' ages on this chart. We'll start by writing numbers down one side—numbers for each age. What numbers do you think we will need? Remember, we want to show your ages and the ages of all of your brothers and sisters. What's the youngest age I should write?❹ What's the oldest age I should write?

Record the numbers students agree on. The numbers should represent the age range (youngest to oldest) of the students and their siblings.

Distribute self-stick notes of one particular color and markers. Have each student print his or her name and age on the note, and then stick the note on the chart.

Sample Student Work

Next, distribute self-stick notes of a different color to students who have siblings.

Teaching Notes

❸ **Baby Siblings** There may be baby sisters or brothers who are not yet 1. Discuss where to put these children on your chart. Some students may want to call them "0 years old," and others may argue for "between 0 and 1." Whatever students decide, the important thing is that they determine ways of indicating numbers that are less than 1.

❹ **Maintaining the Chart** As needed, reinforce the self-stick notes with tape or glue to prevent data from falling off. (Later, you will need to glue or tape each note in place in order to preserve the chart.)

Make a note in this new color for each brother and sister you have. Write their names and ages just as you did on your note. You can look at your homework to help you remember how to spell their names or what their ages are. Remember that we are doing only brothers and sisters. Then come up and put those on the chart.

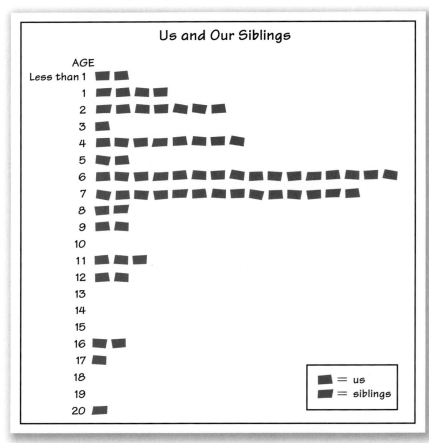

Think about what you notice about these data on our ages and those of our brothers and sisters' ages. Then, find a partner near you and tell each other the things that you have noticed. Here are a couple questions to get you started: What ages have a lot of data? What ages have no data?

Give students a few minutes to talk with a partner about this data set. Then ask students to discuss what they noticed with the whole group.

If the discussion lags, you can point out certain features of the data, comment on them, and encourage students to do likewise. For example:

- There are many [7]s. I wonder why that is? What other numbers have many names beside them? Why do those have so many?

- There are a bunch of numbers where there aren't any names at all. What does that mean?

- Who has the oldest sibling in our class? Who has the youngest?

As the discussion progresses, also ask students about their interpretations of the data. ⑤

- Why do you think there were so many ages for which there are no siblings at all?

- How could there be some 7-year-olds on our chart who are not in this class?

- What numbers have many names beside them? Why do you think they have so many?

- Why are all of your names grouped together and your brothers' and sisters' names scattered?

When you have finished, display this chart in a prominent place and encourage students to continue to examine it.

SESSION FOLLOW-UP

4 Daily Practice and Homework

 Daily Practice: For ongoing review, have students complete *Student Activity Book* page 20.

 Homework: Students analyze a set of data about a group of students on *Student Activity Book* page 21.

 Student Math Handbook: Students and families may use *Student Math Handbook* pages 65, 66, 67, 68 for reference and review. See pages 145–152 in the back of this unit.

Professional Development
⑤ **Dialogue Box:** Us and Our Siblings, p. 143

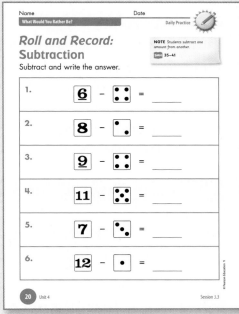

▲ Student Activity Book, p. 20

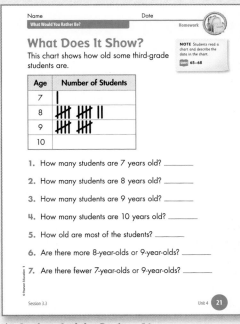

▲ Student Activity Book, p. 21

End-of-Unit Assessment

Math Focus Points

◆ Using attributes to sort a set of objects

◆ Describing and comparing the number of pieces of data in each category or at each value, and interpreting what the data tell you about the group

◆ Understanding that the sum of the pieces of data in all the categories equals the number of people surveyed

Today's Plan		Materials
ACTIVITY **① *Quick Survey:* Curly Hair or Straight Hair?**	10 MIN CLASS	• *Quick Survey* Chart: "Curly or Straight Hair?"*
ASSESSMENT ACTIVITY **② End-of-Unit Assessment**	✔ 50 MIN INDIVIDUALS	• M13–M15*
SESSION FOLLOW-UP **③ Daily Practice**		• *Student Activity Book,* p. 23 • *Student Math Handbook,* pp. 65, 66, 67, 68

*See *Materials to Prepare,* p. 89.

Classroom Routines

Quick Images: Coins Using the set of overhead coins, display 1 quarter, 1 nickel, and 1 dime. Follow the basic *Quick Images* activity. Discuss the quantity and type of coins with the class. Ask questions that focus on identifying each coin and the total number of coins (e.g., What is the name of *this* coin? What do you notice about these coins? How many [nickels] did you see? How many [dimes]? Which coin is not shown?). If time permits, repeat using 3 pennies and 3 nickels.

ACTIVITY

1 *Quick Survey:* Curly Hair or Straight Hair?

10 MIN   CLASS

Post the "Curly Hair or Straight Hair?" *Quick Survey* chart that you have prepared.❶

Do you have curly hair or straight hair?

Record each student's response in the appropriate circle or in the overlap of the circles.

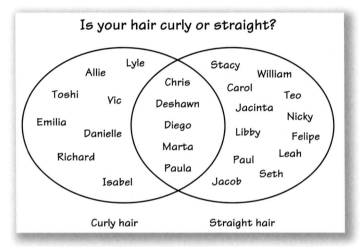

Is your hair curly or straight?

Lyle
Allie
Toshi   Vic
Emilia
Danielle
Richard
Isabel

Chris
Deshawn
Diego
Marta
Paula

Stacy
William
Carol   Teo
Jacinta
Nicky
Libby
Felipe
Paul   Leah
Jacob   Seth

Curly hair   Straight hair

Have a short discussion about the results of the survey. Use questions such as the following to guide the discussion:

• What does this survey tell us about our class?

• How many people have straight hair? How many people have curly hair? How many people have hair that is in between?

• How many people answered the survey?

• What is an equation that can show these data?

In other units in Grade 1, students will have the opportunity to do more quick surveys as a classroom routine.

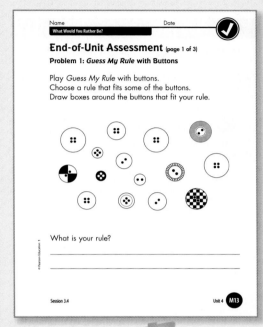

Name _____   Date _____
What Would You Rather Be?

End-of-Unit Assessment (page 1 of 3)
Problem 1: *Guess My Rule* with Buttons

Play *Guess My Rule* with buttons.
Choose a rule that fits some of the buttons.
Draw boxes around the buttons that fit your rule.

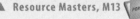

What is your rule?
_____
_____

Session 3.4   Unit 4 M13

▲ **Resource Masters, M13** PORTFOLIO

Teaching Note

❷ Allocating Time Students may need more or less than 50 minutes. Consider allowing students as much time as they need to finish the End-of-Unit Assessment

Professional Development

❸ Teacher Note: End-of-Unit Assessment, p. 129

❹ Assessment in This Unit, p. 14

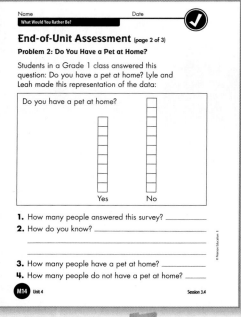

▲ **Resource Masters, M14** PORTFOLIO

ASSESSMENT ACTIVITY

❷ End-of-Unit Assessment Problems

50 MIN INDIVIDUALS

Take a few minutes to explain that the class has come to the end of this unit. You will be exploring some new mathematical ideas tomorrow and over the next few weeks as you turn to Unit 5, *Fish Lengths and Animal Jumps.*

Explain that students will be working on three problems.❷ ❸ Because you would like to get a sense of how much students have grown in their math thinking so far this year, they will work individually.

Problem 1

In the first problem, *Guess My Rule* with Buttons, students name a rule to sort a group of objects and then sort those objects according to that rule. This problem assesses Benchmark 1. Emphasize that students should put squares around the buttons that fit the rule because this is a new way for them to show what buttons fit the rule.❹

ONGOING ASSESSMENT: Observing Students at Work

- **Can students identify a rule that fits some buttons and not others?**

- **Are students able to sort the buttons according to their rule?**

DIFFERENTIATION: Supporting the Range of Learners

ELL If an English Language Learner is unable to put his or her rule into words, allow the student to sort the buttons without naming the rule. Once the buttons are sorted, you can use questions to elicit the rule that the student followed.

- I see you've put squares around these buttons, but not these. Why?

- What makes these buttons similar to each other? How are these buttons the same?

Even if an English Language Learner cannot answer the questions, you should still be able to assess the student's conceptual understanding based on whether or not he or she successfully completes the sorting task.

Problems 2 and 3

In Problems 2 and 3, students examine two representations of two sets of data and determine how many are in each group, which group has more, and how many people were surveyed. These problems assess Benchmarks 3 and 4. Emphasize to students that these representations show data collected from surveys in *other* classes. Their task is to answer questions about the data in these representations. They do not have to answer the survey questions themselves. Some students may find it challenging to work with data that are not about them or that they did not collect.

Students complete questions about representations of data.

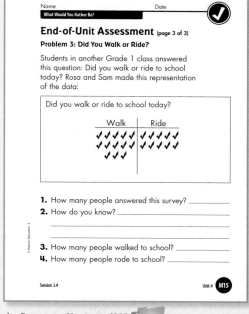

Name _____ Date _____
What Would You Rather Be?

End-of-Unit Assessment (page 3 of 3)
Problem 3: Did You Walk or Ride?

Students in another Grade 1 class answered this question: Did you walk or ride to school today? Rosa and Sam made this representation of the data:

Did you walk or ride to school today?

Walk	Ride
✓✓✓✓✓	✓✓✓✓✓
✓✓✓✓✓	✓✓✓✓✓
✓✓✓	

1. How many people answered this survey? _____
2. How do you know? _____
_____
_____
3. How many people walked to school? _____
4. How many people rode to school? _____

Session 3.4   Unit 4 M15

▲ Resource Masters, M15 [PORTFOLIO]

ONGOING ASSESSMENT: Observing Students at Work ✓

- **Are students able to read the representation and answer the questions about it?**

- **Can students correctly identify the number of people surveyed?**

- **How do students figure out the total?** Do they count all the yes counts and all the no counts? Do they add the quantities together? Do they use facts they know?

Name_____ Date_____

What Would You Rather Be?

Daily Practice

Fruit Snack

It's Max's turn to bring in the class snack. He wants to bring in fruit, but he can bring only two kinds of fruit. Max asked his classmates what their favorite fruits are.

NOTE Students organize and interpret data.
SMH 65–68

Favorite Fruits

apple	pear	grapes	watermelon	banana
Sacha Neil	Carol Bruce Toshi Libby Talisa	Keena Jacob Edgar	Allie Diego Paula Lyle Vic Leah	Marta DeShawn

What two fruits should Max bring in for the class snack? How do you know?

_____
_____

Session 3.4   Unit 4   23

▲ **Student Activity Book, p. 23**

SESSION FOLLOW-UP

3 Daily Practice

 Daily Practice: For enrichment, have students complete *Student Activity Book* page 23.

Student Math Handbook: Students and families may use *Student Math Handbook* pages 65, 66, 67, 68 for reference and review. See pages 145–152 in the back of this unit.

Professional Development

UNIT 4

What Would You Rather Be?

In Part 6 of *Implementing Investigations in Grade 1,* you will find a set of Teacher Notes that addresses topics and issues applicable to the curriculum as a whole rather than to specific curriculum units. They include the following:

Computational Fluency and Place Value

Computational Algorithms and Methods

Representations and Contexts for Mathematical Work

Foundations of Algebra in the Elementary Grades

Discussing Mathematical Ideas

Racial and Linguistic Diversity in the Classroom:
    What Does Equity Mean in Today's Math Classroom?

Teacher Note

Sorting and Classifying

Sorting and classifying is a central scientific, mathematical, and human activity. Important issues of classification arise in many disciplines: How can we classify the books in a library in a systematic and useful way? Is this animal a new species or is it part of a class of animals that has already been identified and described? As children learn about their world, their community, and their language and culture, they are developing and organizing categories of information.

- Which foods are fruits?

- Which animals are dogs?

- Which behaviors are accepted at my house, at grandma's house, or in the park?

- For which words can you add -ed to indicate past tense?

In mathematics, as in other areas, classification is an important activity. Shapes are classified by particular attributes, such as number of sides or faces and types of angles: a triangle is a polygon with three sides. Numbers are classified by particular characteristics as well: a prime number is a number with exactly two factors, 1 and the number itself. Classifications must often be developed for collecting data: for example, for a rating scale of 1–5, how is a *1* defined, and how is a *5* defined?

In the broadest sense, classification is about how things (people, animals, numbers, shapes, attitudes) are alike or different. Sorting any collection into categories requires attending to certain attributes and ignoring others. It is this skill of focusing on particular attributes to the exclusion of others that primary grade students are learning. For example, in order to identify a shape as a triangle, we attend only to certain characteristics—the number of sides and angles, the fact that each side is a line segment, and the fact that the shape is closed (there are no breaks or gaps). We do not pay attention to the size, color, texture, or orientation of the shape in order to identify it as a triangle. What to pay attention to and what to ignore

may seem obvious to adults in this instance. However, the whole idea of classifying by particular attributes is an important new area for young students. They are beginning to learn how to look at only a particular attribute and ignore the rest, rather than look at the overall combination of attributes.

As Grade 1 students sort a variety of sets, they describe and define their categories. In their data collection work in this unit, students are often working with data that fit into a few clearly defined categories (*whale* and *eagle;* or *6 years old, 7 years old,* and *8 years old*). However, some questions of classification are likely to arise. Even though students start out with a survey question involving two choices, all responses may not fit neatly into the two categories. What if a student says, "I like both," "I don't know," or "I don't like either one," in response to a question such as "Which do you like better, peanut butter and jelly or tuna fish?" Such responses raise important issues about creating categories in data collection. Help students decide what they can do to reflect these data in their representations. Students might be tempted to simply ignore these data. Remind students that these responses are part of the information they are finding out. How can they keep track of these responses and how can they represent them?

In their work sorting a variety of sets of objects, students have more decisions to make about how to define and name their categories. This task is challenging for Grade 1 students, especially when they work with sets that have a great deal of variation, such as buttons. For example, there is much room for discussion about which buttons are small or which buttons are shiny. Categories like these raise legitimate problems of definition and clarification that can stimulate deeper thinking about classification and need not be simplified for students. For example, during *Guess My Rule,* some students chose the category "buttons that are small." When they began to field other students' guesses, they found that they could not really agree on which buttons did and did not fit their rule. In a situation like this one, your role is to help students clarify their rule by asking them which objects do and do not belong in their category and why that is the case. Challenge their choices and help them verbalize their reasons. Clarifying a definition of a category is part of learning about classification.

In later grades, as they do more work with categorical data, students will encounter many questions about classifying data. For example, in a survey about favorite books, different views of the data become apparent when the data are classified in different ways: according to author, according to fiction or nonfiction, according to a classification scheme focused on content (adventure, history, fantasy, nature, and so on), or according to age of the reader.

Sorting and classifying is a compelling and challenging topic for Grade 1 students. It is one that they will have many more opportunities to explore through experiences in both mathematics and science.

Guess My Rule

Guess My Rule is a classification game in which players try to figure out the common characteristic of a set of people or objects. As students play *Guess My Rule,* they are choosing attributes by which to sort (color, shape, size), deciding on criteria for their categories (which buttons go in the *small* group, which go in the *big* group?), and looking carefully at what a group of objects has in common.

How to Play

To play the game, the rule maker (who may be you, a student, or a small group) decides on a secret rule for classifying a particular group of things. The rule maker starts the game by showing examples of people or objects that fit the rule. For example, to start a game of *Guess My Rule* with People, with a secret rule of "wearing blue," you can ask two students who are wearing blue to stand up in the front of the room. The players then try to find other individuals who might fit the rule: "Does Allie fit your rule?" If Allie is wearing blue, she joins the students standing in the front. If she does not, she starts a new group standing somewhere else in the room. Both groups must be clearly visible to the players so that they can make use of all the evidence to figure out what the rule is. You will need to stress two guidelines during play.

- **"Wrong" guesses are clues and can be just as important as "right" guesses**. "No, Bruce doesn't fit, but that's important evidence. Think about how he is different from Nicky, Teo, and Diego."

  This is a way to help students learn that errors can be important sources of information.

- **When you think you know what the rule is, test your theory by giving another example, not by revealing the rule**. "Marta, you look as though you're sure you know what the rule is. We don't want to give it away yet, so let's test out your theory. Tell me who else you think fits the rule." Requiring students to add new evidence rather than make a guess serves two purposes. It allows

students to test their theories without revealing their guess to other students, and it provides more information and more time to think for students who do not yet have a theory.

Choosing Rules

When students begin choosing rules, they sometimes think of rules that are either too inclusive ("wearing different colors") or too hard to guess ("has a piece of thread hanging from his shirt"). Guide and support students in choosing rules that are "medium-hard"—not so obvious that everyone will see them immediately, but not so hard that no one will be able to figure them out.

Help students choose rules that will result in sorting the objects or people into at least two groups. If everyone fits the rule or if no one fits the rule, students will not have enough evidence on which to base their reasoning. This guideline eliminates rules that everyone will fit, such as "wearing different colors." It is also important to pick a rule about something that people can observe. One rule for classifying might be "likes baseball," but no one will be able to guess this rule by just looking.

Guessing Rules

Guess My Rule can be dramatic. Keep the mystery and drama high with your remarks. "That was an important clue!" "This is very tricky." "I think Diego has a good idea now." "I bet I know what Nicky's theory is."

Finding one common characteristic of a group of people or objects can be challenging. It is surprising how hard it can be to guess what seems to you to be an obvious rule (such as "wearing green"). You cannot always predict which rules will be difficult. Sometimes a rule that you think will be challenging is guessed right away; other times, a rule that seems obvious will turn out to be very difficult for your students. Give additional clues when students are truly stuck.

Some attributes require students to think harder about how to distinguish between categories. Rules such as "wears glasses" (for people) or "has four holes" (for buttons) are straightforward. Other rules, such as "big" or "shiny," must be defined in relationship to some set of criteria, often in relation to what else is in the set. Ask students to think through and describe how they are making decisions: How did you decide which buttons fit the rule "small"?

Sometimes students who are guessing rules use different words from those that the rule makers had in mind. For example, one pair of Grade 1 students, whose rule was "buttons that are shiny" did not accept student guesses of "reflecting buttons," "metallic buttons," or "gold and silver buttons." The teacher helped the players and the rule-makers explore together whether their definitions were really different. In this case, the rule makers admitted that "reflecting buttons" are shiny, but they presented a good case that "gold and silver buttons" may leave out certain "shiny" buttons (such as copper or jeweled buttons). Encourage the clarification of real differences in definition but discourage rule makers from being too rigid about what they accept as correct guesses. If other students have guessed the concept and have accurately described the characteristics of the category, the exact wording should not be an issue.

Classification is a process used in many disciplines, and you can easily adapt *Guess My Rule* to other subject areas. Animals, books, vehicles, tools, types of food, and many other sets can all be classified in different ways.

Teacher Note

Grade 1 Students' Representations of Data

A representation of data is a way for students to keep track of their data and a way to communicate the results of data collection and analysis. Put simply, in the words of one student, "It shows the data." There are many standard forms of data representation, such as charts, tallies, line plots, and bar graphs. There are also many less standard and less familiar forms of graphs and diagrams that have been invented and are still being invented by statisticians and others to represent particular kinds of data sets. A good representation is not only a means of communication to others but is itself also a tool for better understanding the data.

In the primary grades, students' first uses of data representations should reflect the same central goal: to find ways of showing the data that help, the students themselves and then others "see" better what the data show. Grade 1 students' representations do not necessarily follow the conventions of graphing that older students and adults use. Often Grade 1 students use pictures to show each piece of data, but the pictures may vary in size and may not line up evenly, making it difficult to count quickly and to compare the sizes of different groups. These early attempts at representing data do, however, convey information in a way that is meaningful to the student and to others as well. For example, Carol made two columns, headed "E" for "eagle" and "W" for "whale," and listed the names of each student in the appropriate column. Her representation

clearly shows the two different choices, and she has written the numbers for each choice at the bottom of each column, so we can see the results of the survey at a glance.

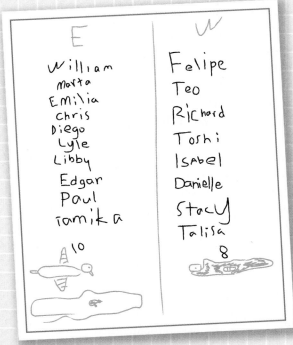

Carol's Work

Similarly, Jacob's chart about baseball and swimming uses symbols to show his data clearly.

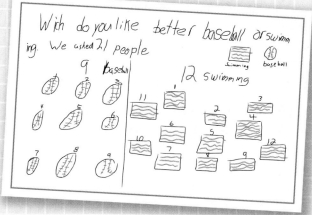

Jacob's Work

Several representations that provide visual images of useful ways to show data are introduced in this unit. For example, in Investigation 2, the class uses two towers of connecting cubes, one in one color to show who wants to be a whale and one in another color to show who wants to be an eagle. Lining up the two cube towers provides a representation that allows direct comparison of the two quantities: it is easy to tell right away which tower is taller. The *Quick Survey* routines throughout the unit introduce representations that use objects, charts with two columns, picture graphs, tallies, bar graphs, and Venn diagrams. Interpreting these representations helps students learn about ways to show data effectively, although they are not yet expected to use all of these representations themselves. If Grade 1 students are prematurely asked to represent their data in standard forms, they often produce graphs that, for them, do not communicate anything about their data. As when following any poorly understood procedure, making a graph the way it is "supposed to" look can result in students' losing their sense of what the data convey. However, students may begin to incorporate some elements of the representations they see into their own.

By inventing their own representations, students become more familiar with their data and remain clear about what their pictures or graphs represent. Then, through discussing and comparing these representations, as in the discussion at the end of Session 2.2, students consider what features of a representation help communicate a clear description of the data. For example, in the **Dialogue Box:** Sharing Survey Findings, page 141, students discuss what they can notice easily from different representations, how they can tell what the numbers on the representations mean, and how the use of color on one representation helps distinguish girls' and boys' responses.

Vic's, Bruce's, Paula's, and Emilia's work represents attempts to organize the data in a way that makes it easier to compare the different responses to their surveys.

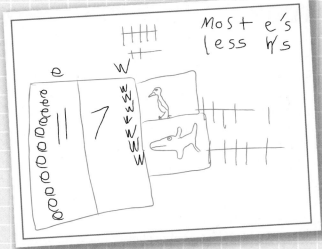

Vic's Work

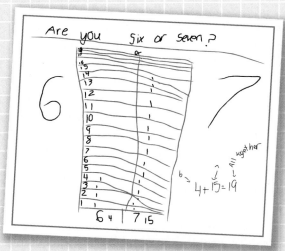

Bruce's Work

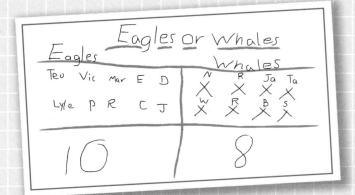

Paula's Work

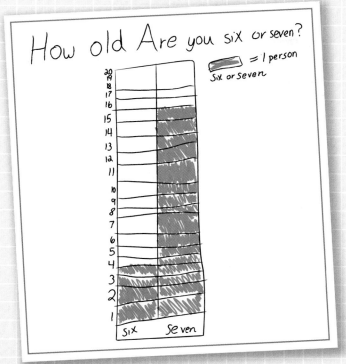

Emilia's Work

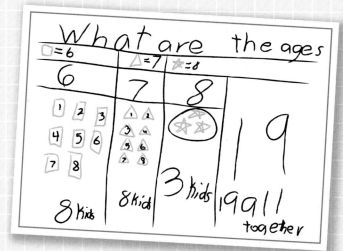

Allie's Work

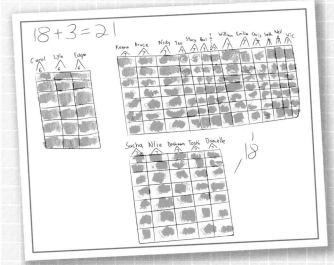

Lyle's Work

In Investigation 3, students represent numerical data—the ages of themselves and their siblings. Numerical data introduce further complexity because representing these data involves two different kinds of quantities—the values of the pieces of data and how many pieces of data are at each value (the frequency of each value). Students will focus on these ideas in Grade 2, but students' representations in Grade 1 may begin to show that they are trying to sort out what the different numbers mean. For example, Allie's representation of the ages of students in the class is similar to many Grade 1 students' representations of categorical data. Lyle, on the other hand, seems to be thinking about how to show the meaning of both the numbers that represent the ages (*6* years old and *7* years old) and the numbers that represent the number of people at each age (*18* people who are 7 years old and *3* people who are 6 years old).

When you talk with students about their representations, ask questions such as these:

- How did you keep track of everyone in the class? Can you tell whether your representation has a piece of data for each student you surveyed?

- How would someone else tell from your representation how many students [chose "eagle"]?

- What did you find out from your survey? How does your representation show that?

Teacher Note

Describing Data

After students have collected and represented their data, the next essential part of their work is to describe what the data show. The key question in describing data in this unit is this: What do these data tell us about our class [the class next door, our siblings]? In the context of this overall question, Grade 1 students' descriptions focus on the following two characteristics of the data:

- What is the number of pieces of data in each category or at each value? (How many people wanted to be eagles? How many people are 7 years old?)

- Which category has more data? (Did more people want to be eagles or whales?)

In addition, students consider the sum of the data in all categories and its relationship to the total number of students in the class: "If there are 24 students in the class, and everyone was here on the day we took the survey, then we should have 24 pieces of data in all the categories together."

What is most critical for young students is to keep connecting their data, and the representations of their data, to what it represents. Students can easily become focused on the number of check marks or pictures or other symbols they have made and lose track of what these symbols represent. For example, if a student says, "I made 18 stars and 5 circles," it is important to ask a question such as "What do those stars tell me about the class? How would someone looking at your paper know that the stars are people who are 7 years old?" In the **Dialogue Box:** Sharing Survey Findings, page 141, the teacher engages students in clarifying what the numbers on one of the posters represent.

In Grade 1, expect that students' descriptions of their data will be straightforward, focusing on which choice got the most responses, as in Isabel's and Teo's writing about their surveys.

Would you rather get a shot from the doctor or get a bee sting? I lerned that more peopol wanted a shot then a bee sting and 5 peopol want a bee sting and 15 peopol want a shot.

Isabel's Work

Wod you rather hav super streth or a super bran? More pieypl wod rater have a super bran.

Teo's Work

Some students may think of ways to get more information from their data. For example, Felipe broke down this data further into which responses came from boys and which from girls:

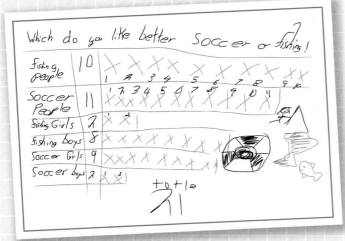

Felipe's Work

Throughout this unit, and especially during the work on their own survey questions in Investigation 2, help students think about what they can learn from their data. Does their data give them information about their original question? Were there unexpected responses? What did they do about those responses? What surprised them about their data? What did they learn about the group they surveyed?

Comparing two groups heightens the need for describing data and, through comparison and contrast, helps students notice features of the data. Comparing the ages of students in your class with the ages of students in another Grade 1 class helps your students describe the data more clearly. After students have completed their own surveys, some may be interested in carrying out the same survey in another class, representing those data, and comparing the results from the two groups.

Assessment: "Deep Sea or Outer Space?" Representations

Problem 1

Benchmark addressed:

Benchmark 2: Represent a set of data with two categories.

In order to meet the benchmark, students' work should show that they can:

- Organize a set of collected data into distinct categories;

- Represent the data so that it communicates the results of the survey.

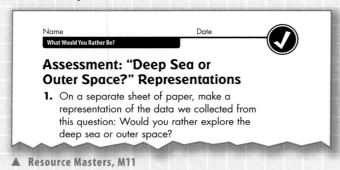

Name   Date
What Would You Rather Be?

Assessment: "Deep Sea or Outer Space?" Representations

1. On a separate sheet of paper, make a representation of the data we collected from this question: Would you rather explore the deep sea or outer space?

▲ **Resource Masters, M11**

Meeting the Benchmark

The following examples of student work provide a range of typical responses. All of these students meet the benchmark—they have organized and accurately represented the set of data. However, they have used a variety of ways to represent it.

Allie has organized the data into two distinct categories: Deep Sea and Outer Space. She has represented the data by creating two labeled columns and writing the names of the students under their corresponding response. Allie has also numbered the people and written the total number of pieces of data in each category. It is easy to tell from Allie's representation which category has more pieces of data.

Allie's Work

When collecting and representing data, who gave which response is as important for some students as how many people gave each response. These students are likely to include the names of the students in their representation. Some may write only the names and not the number of responses in each category.

Like Allie, Paul and Carol have organized the data into two distinct categories. They have represented the data in two columns and represented students' responses with pictures, rather than representing who gave which response. Both students have written the number of pieces of data in each category and Carol has also numbered each piece of data. Paul's and Carol's pictorial representations show what the survey is about, but it is not as easy to compare the sizes of the categories.

Some Grade 1 students gravitate toward representing a set of categorical data by using pictures because it is an easy way to show what the data they are representing are about. When creating pictorial representations, some write the numbers of the responses in each category, and others do not.

Jacinta and Marta have chosen to represent the data in a less direct way than Paul and Carol or Allie, who used pictures or names. Marta represented the data with towers of squares and Jacinta made a bar graph (as well as a pictorial representation). Both have numbered each piece of data, written the total in each category, and written the total number of responses. It is easy to tell which category has more pieces of data, especially in Marta's representation, in which each square is close to the same size.

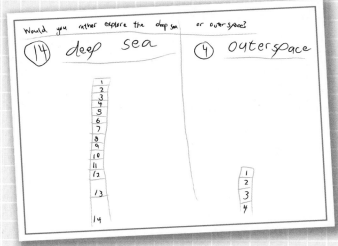

Marta's Work

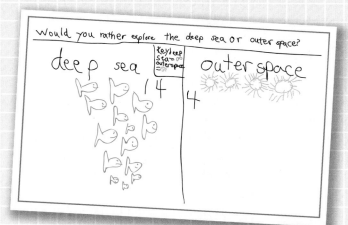

Paul's response

Jacinta's Work

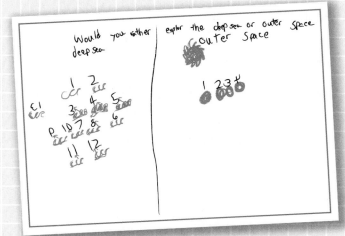

Carol's Work

Partially Meeting the Benchmark

Some students will organize and represent the data clearly but may not include all of the pieces of data. Finding a way to ensure that all the pieces of data are included in a representation of that data is an important element of making a representation. Students who have missed pieces of data could benefit from discussing how they could keep track of the data and make sure that all of the data is in their representation.

Not Meeting the Benchmark

Students who do not meet Benchmark 2 may still be constructing what it means to work with data.

Some students may, like Leah, only copy the data in the format it was given to them:

Leah's work

Other students like Stacy may only write a statement about the data:

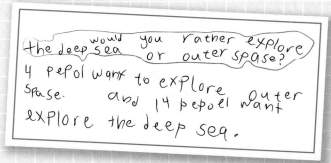

Stacy's Work

Students may not organize their data into distinct categories or may just write the quantity in each category. There is information that can be gathered from each of these responses, but they are not, in fact, representations of the data.

These students may not yet understand what the purpose of making a representation is or how to organize a set of data and make a representation that communicates information to others. All students will have more opportunities in this unit to represent sets of data. As the students who did not meet the benchmark in this assessment create representations, help them focus on a representation as a means of communicating information by asking questions such as these:

- How can you show someone not in this class what we found out?

- What will someone not in this class be able to find out from your representation?

- How can you make a representation so that it is easy to see that [12 people are 6 years old and 14 people are 7]?

- Can you show that 10 people are 6 and 12 are 7?

Problems 2 and 3

Benchmarks addressed:

Benchmark 3: Interpret a variety of representations of data with two categories.

Benchmark 4: Describe a set of data, including how many are in each group, which group is greater, and how many people responded to the survey.

In order to meet the benchmarks, students' work should show that they can:

- Use their representation to state what they found out from the data about the group surveyed;

- Use their representation to interpret the data by stating what interested them or surprised them about the data.

> **2.** What did you find out from this survey?
>
> _____
> _____
> _____
> _____
> _____
>
> **3.** What surprised or interested you?
>
> _____
> _____
> _____
> _____
> _____
> _____
>
> Session 2.5　　　　　　　　　　Unit 4　**M11**

▲ Resource Masters, M11

Meeting the Benchmarks

2. What did you find out from this survey?

In response to Problem 2, most students compare the number of pieces of data in each category.

Some students, like Nicky, write about the number of pieces of data in each category

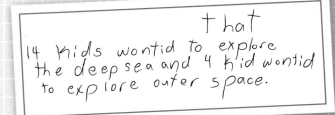

14 kids wontid to explore that the deep sea and 4 kid wontid to explore outer space.

Nicky's Work

Other students, like Bruce, write which category has more pieces of data.

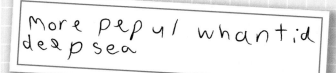

More pepul whantid deep sea

Bruce's Work

A few students, like Felipe, gather and write about less evident information from the data.

13 wanted Deep Sea. 4 wanted Outer Space. 7 girls wanted Deep Sea. 6 boys did. 3 boys wanted Outer Space. 1 girl did.

Felipe's Work

3. What surprised or interested you?

In response to this question, students share their own thoughts about the data. Many students, like Allie, write about how the results were different from what they had expected.

I thot mor Pepull wod like Space than Sea.

Allie's Work

Partially Meeting the Benchmarks

Some students, like Lyle, may write statements that tell what they noticed in the representation, but do not refer to what the information tells about the people surveyed.

thar are 13 on sea and 9 on space

Lyle's Work

From this statement, it is unclear whether Lyle understands the connection between a representation and what it tells about the people surveyed. Lyle's teacher may ask him what *13 on sea* and *9 on space* tells him about his class. If he responds, for example, "13 people wanted to explore the sea and 9 wanted to explore space," Lyle would meet the benchmark.

Not Meeting the Benchmarks

Students who do not meet Benchmarks 3 or 4 may still be constructing what it means to work with data.

Students may make statements that do not relate to the data as did Teo.

14 has The NUMber 4 in it.

Teo's Work

Alternatively, they may come to incorrect conclusions or they may not respond at all to one or both questions.

These students may not yet be able to make sense of a data representation or may not know how to gather information from a representation. All students will have more opportunities to read, interpret, and describe data in this unit. The students who do not meet the benchmark in this assessment may need more support in figuring out what to look for. As students continue to use representations to describe and interpret data, you can help them work on these aspects by asking them questions such as these:

- What can you tell from this representation?

- Can you figure out how many people are 7 in this class by looking at this representation?

- Did this survey turn out the way you thought it would?

End-of-Unit Assessment

Problem 1: *Guess My Rule* with Buttons

Benchmark addressed:

Benchmark 1: Sort a group of objects according to a given attribute.

In order to meet the benchmark, students' work should show that they can:

- Choose and record a rule that applies to some of the buttons;

- Sort the buttons according to the rule they chose by putting a box around the buttons that fit the rule.

In this problem, students choose a rule to sort the buttons. They write their rule and then sort the buttons by putting squares around the buttons that fit their rule.

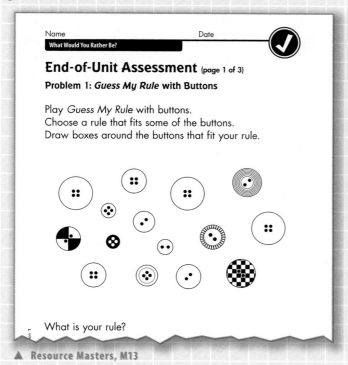

▲ Resource Masters, M13

Meeting the Benchmark

In your students' solutions to this problem, look for the following:

They have identified one rule that fits some of the buttons. They have correctly put boxes around those buttons that fit the rule. Some possible rules students may identify are these: 2 holes, 4 holes, buttons with designs on them, white buttons, buttons with mostly black. In these student work examples, Paula correctly put squares around the buttons that fit her rule, which was "it has to hav a desin on it." Diego also indicated which buttons did not fit his rule which was "only 2 dots" with arrows.

Paula's Work

Diego's Work

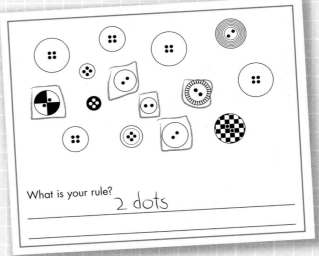

Chris's Work

Partially Meeting the Benchmark

Students may identify a rule that correctly fits some of the buttons but may not correctly sort the buttons according to that rule. They may leave out some buttons that fit their rule as Isabel and Chris did or may misidentify a button as fitting their rule.

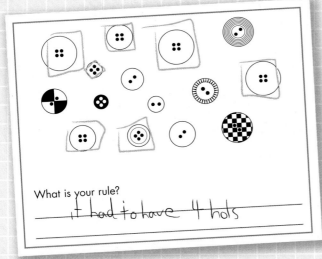

Isabel's Work

Some of these students may have simply missed a button when they were putting boxes around the ones that fit the rule. To help determine whether this was just a mistake or a lack of understanding, ask these students to check whether they put a box around all of the buttons that fit their rule. If they correct their mistakes, they have met the benchmark.

If they do not correct their mistakes, there may be some aspects of sorting by attributes that they are still working on. These students may have some understanding of how to sort objects according to one attribute. They are able to identify an appropriate rule that fits some buttons, but they may not yet understand how to sort the buttons solely by the one rule they have chosen. They may notice that a button is similar to one that fits the rule in *other* ways and include it or they may decide that a button does not fit their rule because it does not seem similar enough to other ones that fit the rule.

Not Meeting the Benchmark

A few students may not be able to identify one rule that fits some of the buttons. They may identify more than one rule (black buttons and white buttons), or they may put together only buttons that are exactly the same. Students who do not meet the benchmark may not yet understand how to sort by one attribute and may not be able to focus on one attribute of an object and compare how that attribute is similar or different in other objects. Students who do not meet the benchmark need to continue to have opportunities to sort objects. You might provide more opportunities during Math Workshops in later units for students to sort objects according to an attribute you tell them, to figure out the attribute you have sorted objects by, or to play *Guess My Rule*.

Problems 2 and 3: Do You Have a Pet at Home? and Did You Walk or Ride?

Benchmarks addressed:

Benchmark 3: Interpret a variety of data representations with two categories.

Benchmark 4: Describe a set of data, including how many are in each group, which group is greater, and how many people responded to the survey.

In order to meet the benchmarks, students' work should show that they can:

- Use the representations to respond correctly to the questions about how many pieces of data are in each group and how many people responded to the survey;

- Explain how they figured out how many people responded to the survey.

In Problems 2 and 3, students read representations of data collected in other classrooms. They answer questions about the amount of data in each group and how many people responded to the survey.

Name _____ Date _____

What Would You Rather Be?

End-of-Unit Assessment (page 2 of 3)

Problem 2: Do You Have a Pet at Home?

Students in a Grade 1 class answered this question: Do you have a pet at home? Lyle and Leah made this representation of the data:

Do you have a pet at home?

Yes   No

1. How many people answered this survey? _____
2. How do you know? _____
   _____
   _____
3. How many people have a pet at home? _____
4. How many people do not have a pet at home? _____

M14 Unit 4   Session 3.4

© Pearson Education 1

▲ Resource Masters, M14

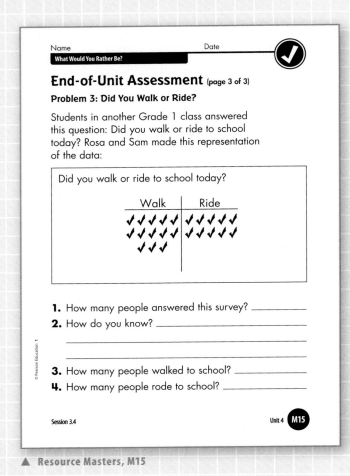

▲ **Resource Masters, M15**

Meeting the Benchmarks

All students who meet the benchmarks use the representation in Problem 2 and the representation in Problem 3 to correctly figure out how many people have a pet at home (how many people rode to school) and how many people do not have a pet at home (how many people walked to school). They correctly figure out how many people answered the survey and explain how they knew how many people answered the survey.

Students figure out how many people answered the survey in a variety of ways: For example, Libby counted all of the squares and the number of squares in each group, and Tamika used combinations she knew to find the total of both groups. Other students may count on from the first group or count the responses by 2s or 5s. All students should understand that they are able to figure out the number of people who answered the survey by finding the total pieces of data in both categories together.

Diego's Work

Partially Meeting the Benchmarks

Some students may incorrectly count the number of pieces of data. Teachers may want to keep track of whether these students often miscount when they are asked to count and decide whether the student is having trouble with counting. However, this is an issue related to counting and not to working with data.

Some students may be able to use the representation to correctly figure out how many people gave each response but may not be able to figure out how many people answered the survey. These students may not yet understand that the sum of the pieces of data in each category should equal the number of people surveyed.

Seth is able to use the representation to figure out how many people gave each response, but he says that 21 people answered the survey "because there's 21 people in our class."

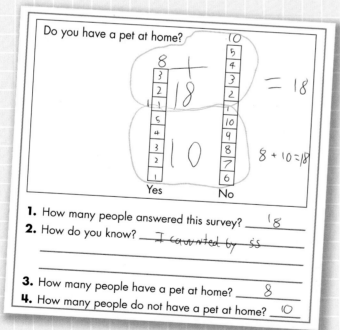

Do you have a pet at home?

1. How many people answered this survey? __18__
2. How do you know? __I put nubrst__

3. How many people have a pet at home? __8__
4. How many people do not have a pet at home? __10__

Libby's Work

Do you have a pet at home?

1. How many people answered this survey? __18__
2. How do you know? __I counted by 5s__

3. How many people have a pet at home? __8__
4. How many people do not have a pet at home? __10__

Tamika's Work

Do you have a pet at home?

1. How many people answered this survey? __21__
2. How do you know? __Becoes Thaius 21 people in ave clas__

3. How many people have a pet at home? __8__
4. How many people do not have a pet at home? __10__

Seth's Work

Seth may not yet understand that the sum of the pieces of data in each category should equal the number of people surveyed, or he may be confused about how this data could be about another class and thinks it should be about his own class.

Not Meeting the Benchmarks

A few students may be unable to answer the questions posed about the data or may give answers that do not relate to the representation. These students may not yet understand how to read a representation or gather information from a representation. They may not be able to relate the representation to what it tells them about the results to a survey or about the respondents to the survey.

It may be difficult for some Grade 1 students to move from doing a survey in their own class to looking at a representation of data gathered from another class and realizing that it represents data that is not from their own class. It may help them for you to continue to emphasize that this is data from another class. It may also help students to make sense of this by giving them experiences of collecting and representing data themselves from another class and then describing the data.

Students who do not meet Benchmarks 3 and 4 need more experience reading representations of data and describing the information they can gather from those representations. They need more experiences with representations of data collected from their own class as well as data collected from outside their class. As they work on reading representations and describing the data, you can support them by asking questions such as the folowing:

- What can you find out from this representation about people's responses to the question ["Do you like spinach?"]?

- You said that there are 10 checks under "No." What does that tell you about people's responses to the question ["Do you like spinach?"]?

- What does this representation tell you about [Ms. Wright's] class's response to this survey question?

Dialogue Box

They're All Different Sizes

Students in this class began the discussion Describing Shapes in Session 1.1 by sharing words that describe the Power Polygons they have been looking at. The teacher has written each of their description words on a self-stick note and put each on the chart paper labeled "Shapes."

Teacher: You came up with many different words that describe these shapes. Let's look for a minute at these words. I noticed that many of you described the number of sides. Can you find some words that describe the number of sides?

Emilia: 4 sides.

Lyle: 3 sides.

Jacob: Square.

Marta 6 sides.

The teacher writes "Number of Sides" on the left-hand corner of the chart paper and places all the self-stick notes that students mention under "Number of Sides."

Teacher: Do all of these words describe the number of sides?

Nicky: No, square doesn't. Square isn't the number of sides.

Jacob: A square has 4 sides.

Nicky: Yes, but it doesn't tell you about sides.

Jacob: Yes, it tells me that there are 4 and they are all the same!

Teacher: If something is a square, you know that it has 4 sides, but square might also go together with some other words. Are there other words that might go together with square?

Bruce: That's the only square.

Teacher: That's true, but are there other words that are similar, that describe a similar thing? For example, up here we have 4 sides, 3 sides, 6 sides altogether that describe the number of sides. What does square describe?

Seth: The name?

Carol: The shape?

Teacher: What do you think? Does square describe the name? Does it describe the shape?

Isabel: I think it tells the shape, but it's the name of it.

The teacher writes "Shape" in the upper right-hand corner of the chart.

Teacher: What other words describe the shapes of these Power Polygons?

Lyle: Rectangle.

Paula: Like a hat.

Leah: Hexagon.

The teacher puts these self-stick notes under the word "shape."

Teacher: Do you agree that all of these words describe the shapes of the Power Polygons?

Class: Yes!

Teacher: When you were describing the number of sides of the Power Polygons, you were describing an attribute of the Power Polygons. You were also describing an attribute of the Power Polygons when you described the shape of them. What other attributes did you describe?

Silence.

Teacher: What other words up here do you think go together?

Paula: Big and small.

Teacher: Why do those go together?

Paula: Because they're big and small.

Teacher: Does anyone know what attribute big and small are describing? What is *big* or *small* telling you about one of these shapes?

Isabel: That they're big or small?

Emilia: They could be medium, too.

Felipe: They're all different sizes—small or big or medium or even tiny!

Teacher: Could I write "size" up here? Do people agree? Do small and big describe the size of the Power Polygons?

Class: Yes.

The students in this class described many important attributes of the Power Polygons and were able to use specific words, such as *big, small, square,* or *3 sides,* to describe the shapes. However, they may not yet have many ideas about how these words can be grouped into broader categories of attributes such as *size, shape,* and *number of sides.* In this discussion, the teacher helped students group the descriptive words and then name the attribute by starting with what they knew already and by asking all of the students to discuss and agree on the groupings and the attributes.

Guess My Rule with Partners

Students play *Guess My Rule* with collections of objects during Math Workshop in sessions 1.3 and 1.4. This is the first time this class played *Guess My Rule* on their own with partners.

Vic, Libby, and Carol are playing *Guess My Rule* with buttons. The teacher is working with them. Vic made a rule and told it to the teacher. He puts two buttons on the mat that says "These Fit My Rule" and two on the mat that says "These Don't Fit My Rule."

Teacher: Libby, can you pick one to find out whether it fits Vic's rule?

Libby: [holds up a button] Does this fit your rule?

Teacher: Libby, can you put the button where you think it belongs—either on the mat that says "These Fit My Rule" or the mat that says, "These Don't Fit My Rule"? Then Vic will tell us whether it is in the right place.

Libby puts the button on the "These Fit My Rule" mat and Vic shakes his head and places it on the "These Don't Fit My Rule" mat.

Teacher: Now, Carol, you go.

Carol: [holds up a button] Does this fit your rule?

Teacher: Carol, can you put the button where you think it goes?

Carol and Libby go through five more turns each. By their third turn, they start to understand the flow of the game and begin to put the button they choose in the pile where they think it belongs and then wait for Vic to tell them whether they are correct. At the end, Carol correctly guesses Vic's rule, which is 4-holed buttons.

Teacher: Let's play again. Libby, come tell me your rule [Libby whispers her rule to the teacher]. Now show us some buttons that fit the rule and two that don't fit.

Libby picks two buttons that fit her rule and two that do not fit.

Carol puts a 2-holed button on the "These Fit My Rule" mat.

Libby: No, that doesn't fit my rule.

Carol: Yes, it does.

Teacher: Libby is telling you that it doesn't, but what did you think her rule was?

Carol: 2 holes.

Teacher: Libby, is that the rule?

Libby: No.

Vic and Carol take a few more turns.

Vic: I know your rule; it's purple.

Teacher: Libby, is that your rule?

Libby: Yes.

Tamika and Teo are playing *Guess My Rule* with shapes. Teo has put two orange squares of the same size on the sheet that says "These Fit My Rule" and two other shapes on the sheet that says "These Don't Fit My Rule."

Tamika: Does this fit the rule? [Puts a blue rectangle on "These Fit My Rule"]

Teo takes the blue rectangle off that sheet and puts it on the other sheet. Tamika puts a red triangle on the sheet that says "These Don't Fit My Rule."

Tamika: Is this where this goes? [Teo nods his head.]

Tamika tries a few more. The two orange squares are still the only ones on the "These Fit My Rule" sheet. There are blue rectangles and triangles of all different colors on the "These Don't Fit My Rule" sheet.

Tamika: So the rule is they have to be the same?

Teo: Not just the same. [He looks into the container and starts pulling out shapes. He puts a large yellow square on the paper on the "These Fit My Rule" sheet.]

Tamika: So the rule is squares!

Tamika and Teo put all the shapes back and begin again. Tamika puts a blue rectangle and an orange square on the "These Fit My Rule" sheet. She puts a yellow hexagon and an orange triangle on the "These Don't Fit My Rule" sheet.

Tamika: Can you guess my rule?

Teo: Blue and orange?

Tamika: Nope.

Teo takes a few more turns. A yellow square has been added to the "These Fit My Rule" sheet.

Teo: I think I know. It's only squares and rectangles.

Tamika: Not really [puts out a rhombus, a rectangle, and a triangle in an area not on either paper]. Can you tell something about these?

Teo: You mean they all fit?

Tamika: No, this is the one that doesn't fit [points to the triangle]. How are these two the same and this one different?

Teo: Umm.

Tamika: They both have 4 corners.

William and Marta are playing *Guess My Rule* with shapes. They have already sorted a number of shapes. There are only blue shapes on the "These Fit My Rule" sheet. There are a variety of shapes on the "These Don't Fit My Rule" sheet.

Teacher: What do you think the rule is William?

William: I don't even know what her rule is.

Teacher: Take a look at these [points to the ones that fit the rule] and ask yourself a question. What question could you ask yourself about these that fit the rule?

William: Does it have to have sides?

Teacher: Do you notice something about all of these that fit the rule?

William: Does it have to be blue?

Teacher: How did you know that the rule was blue? Did you look at the ones that don't fit the rule as well?

William: No.

Marta: These are the same triangles but the one that fits is blue and the one that doesn't is green.

Teacher: William, how did you know it wasn't triangles?

William: Because there's a rectangle and a rhombus and a triangle that fit the rule.

Teacher: How did the ones that don't fit the rule help you?

William: Because there's no blue over there.

As these students play *Guess My Rule,* they are figuring out how to play the game and use the clues of what has already been sorted to help them. Some students have difficulty focusing on just one attribute for choosing a rule or determining a rule. Through the teachers' questions and sometimes the help of a partner, many students are able to focus more clearly on one attribute and what to look for to help them determine the rule.

Discussing "Eagle or Whale?" Data

This class used connecting cubes to collect their responses to the question "Would you rather be an eagle or a whale for one day?" During the follow-up discussion, the teacher stresses the relationship between the total number of children who participated in the survey and the number who answered in each category.

Teacher: What did we find out from this survey?

Bruce: Jacob and I both wanted to be eagles.

Emilia: I thought Diego would say whale, but he didn't.

Paul: It looks like whales won.

Teacher: What do you mean, whales won?

Paul: More kids wanted to be whales.

Tamika: There were 15 whales.

Emilia: Yeah, but a lot wanted to be eagles, too.

Teacher: How many wanted to be eagles?

Emilia counts the connecting cubes in the tower representing eagles one by one. Another student double-checks the count.

Emilia: There are 12 who wanted to be eagles.

Libby: There are 3 more yellow than blue.

Teacher: How do you know?

Libby: I can tell, there are 3 more yellow sticking up.

Teacher: What does that tell us about people wanting to be eagles or whales?

Libby: 3 more whales.

Teacher: So 15 wanted to be whales, and 12 wanted to be eagles. How many is that altogether?

Marta: I think it's going to be a lot, like maybe 50.

Tamika: It should be 28, because that's how many are in our class.

Felipe: But Sacha is absent!

Bruce: We could count them. Just count every cube up there, and then we'll know for sure.

Teacher: That's one way to see. How else could we find out?

Nicky: We could count us because we all answered the question.

Teacher: Why don't we try both?

The class counts both the cubes and the students in the class. They come up with 27 both times.

Teacher: Why did we come up with 27 both times? Why were there 27 cubes when we counted both the cubes for students who wanted to be whales and the cubes for students who wanted to be eagles, and then there were 27 again when we counted the students?

Nicky: Because the whales plus the eagles are all the kids who answered the question and all of us answered the question.

Teacher: Okay, now let's talk about why you wanted to be an eagle or a whale. Who chose to be a whale? Why did you choose to be a whale, Paula?

Paula: If you were a whale you could be one of the biggest animals in the world, and I like whales.

Teacher: What do you like about whales?

Julia: We could jump in the air really high.

Teacher: Who chose to be an eagle? Why did you choose to be an eagle?

Isabel: Because they can fly.

Toshi: Because they can dive down into the water and get fish and fly really high.

Lyle: Because I love birds.

Teacher: We can learn many different things about people when we collect data.

It is important for students to recognize that the number of "eagles" and the number of "whales" (plus those in any other categories students may have created) add up to the total number of students who answered. Another element of this discussion is a comparison of the numbers in each category. Students often use the terminology "winning" to describe which group is bigger. Emphasizing a student's observation of relative size rather than the competitive notion of winning, as this teacher did, keeps the conversation focused on the mathematics.

Dialogue Box

Sharing Survey Findings

The students in this class are sharing what they found out from the survey questions they asked one another. The teacher asks students to show their representations of their data, and the rest of the students talk about what they notice in these representations. Pairs then discuss what they found out from their surveys and what surprised them. Although longer discussions could have taken place about each representation, the teacher chose to focus on one aspect so that most pairs could share.

Marta and Teo show the class their representation of the data they collected in answer to the question "Which do you like better: swimming or baseball?"

Teo: Marta made Xs for swimming, and I made circles for baseball. Marta numbered 1, 2, 3, 4, 5, 6, 7, 8, 9, 10, 11, 12. And I numbered 1, 2, 3, 4, 5, 6, 7, 8, 9.

Teacher: When you look at this representation, what do you know right away?

Libby: How many people like swimming better than baseball. It was 12 people who liked swimming, and 9 people liked baseball, but I don't know how many people were asked altogether.

Vic and William show their representation to the class.

Vic: Our question was "Would you rather have a gecko or a hermit crab?"

Teacher: By looking at this, do you think you know the results of this survey?

Chris: It's 21.

Teacher: What's 21? What does the 21 stand for?

Chris: The answer to "Do you want to have a hermit crab or a gecko?"

Teacher: I don't understand. What can you tell from this representation?

Nicky: I can tell that 13 people wanted hermit crabs, and 8 people wanted geckos.

Chris: That's 21. 13 people in the class wanted hermit crabs.

Teacher: What does this number over here [points to the 8] mean to you?

Chris: Eight people wanted geckos.

Teacher: Nicky and Diego, what about your survey? Your question was "Would you rather wear pajamas or clothes?" What did you find out or what surprised you?

Nicky: I thought it was surprising that not many kids said PJs.

Diego: Yes, I thought more kids would want to wear their PJs.

Teacher: Seth and Lyle asked, "Would you rather be a bobcat or a fox?" Did anything from your results surprise you?

Lyle: There were more bobcats than foxes, and I thought there would be more kids that would like to be foxes.

Seth: I thought more kids would be bobcats because I heard lots of kids talk about bobcats.

Diego: Can we ask these questions with the second graders?

Teacher: Yes, that sounds like a good idea. I'm sure the Grade 2 teachers would be happy to have you come over and ask some questions of the second graders. Before we talk about how we'll do that, let's finish sharing our surveys. Would you rather be a ghost or a monster? What was so surprising about this survey? [Students are laughing because there is only one monster and 21 ghosts.]

Jacob: There's only one monster.

Teacher: That was surprising to me too. Tamika and Carol asked, "Did you sign up for baseball?" and 12 kids said yes and 10 said no. Did you find anything surprising about that data?

Carol: We thought that more kids would say no.

Paul: I notice that only 3 girls signed up for baseball. [Tamika and Carol have recorded the boys' names in blue and the girls' names in red.]

Teacher: Paul, how did you figure that out so quickly?

Paul: I saw Tamika, Carol, and Nicky, and the girls are all in red.

Teacher: That's very interesting—they decided to put the girls' names in red and the boys' in blue. If we know that there are 3 girls, how many boys signed up for baseball?

Teo: A lot.

Teacher: A lot is a good answer, but can we actually find out the number?

Teo: "There were 12 so 11, 10, 9. Nine."

Teacher: Toshi and Felipe, did you find anything interesting from your survey?

Felipe: We finished and then we counted, and then we knew we needed two more people and I couldn't figure out who we missed, but then Toshi reminded me that we forgot to put *our* answers down.

Teacher: Oh no! That sounds like a good learning mistake. And last but not least, Leah and Jacinta asked, "Would you rather watch cartoons or a movie?" What did you find out?

Jacinta: More kids wanted to watch a movie.

Leah: I know why more kids wanted to watch a movie. It's because you can take videos from a store any time you feel like it but cartoons are on at a certain time.

Dialogue Box

Us and Our Siblings

The class has created a chart of their ages and their siblings' ages. Now they are discussing what they notice about this graph.

Teacher: What do you notice about this chart? First of all, what is it about?

Bruce: Ages.

Marta: Numbers.

Teacher: Whose ages?

Carol: Boys and girls.

Lyle: Your family, but not your moms and dads.

Toshi: Your brothers and sisters.

Teacher: So what does this chart about your *siblings* and your ages show us? Remember that all the yellow notes are your ages and all the blue notes are your siblings' ages.

Libby: Some of them are more and some are less.

Teacher: Which ones are more?

Libby: Those. The 7s.

Teacher: What does that 7 stand for? Why are those people's names next to 7?

Libby: Because they're 7 years old. There are 11 of them.

Teacher: 11 what?

Libby: 11 kids are 7.

Teacher: 11 kids are 7 years old. That's the most on this chart. How many kids who are 7 years old are *not* in our class?

Carol: Two.

Teacher: How could you tell?

Carol: Because it's blue and not yellow. On the 7.

Teacher: People are really curious about who those kids are. Can anyone fill us in?

Seth: My twin sister is next door.

Lyle: My brother is in kindergarten. He just turned 7, and I've been 7 for a long time.

Teacher: What else do you notice?

Jacob: There are 3 people who are 3 years old.

Teacher: And who are they?

Jacob: Siblings. And 3 who are 0, and 3 who are 4, and 3 who are 12.

Chris: This has 2 [points to 22] and 9 has 2 [the teacher records these numbers].

Teacher: Is there any other age that has 2 people?

Jacinta: 5 has 2.

Allie: They are in order from 0 all the way to 22.

Teacher: We organized the chart in order from 0 to 22. Is there anything else you noticed?

Allie: And only 1 group has 0 numbers. And that's 14.

Teacher: I don't agree. Are there other ages that have 0 people?

Emilia: 16, 18, 21.

Teacher: So there is no one who is 14, 16, 18, or 21 years old.

Isabel: I notice that 7 has more than all of them, but the 6 has only 10. And if you put one more it would be 11.

Paula: In the 8 row, 4 people are 8 in this class, and 4 people who are siblings are 8. I notice that 4 + 4 is 8, and all the cards are 8.

Vic: There are more siblings than kids in our class.

Teacher: Why do you think that?

Vic: Because there are only 24 of us and there are more than 24 of them. I just looked at the board, and I raised my hand.

Teacher: But how did you know that there were more than 24 siblings?

Vic: Because—let's count.

Vic goes to the chart and points to each sibling card. The students count by 1s as he points to each blue card; they count 42 siblings.

Teacher: How come there are 42 siblings? How come there are more siblings than just us?

Allie: Because if we want the same amount as them we need more kids.

Teacher: Yes, but why?

Allie: Because some kids in this class have a lot of sisters and brothers and some kids only have a little bit.

Teacher: Are you trying to say that some kids have more than one brother or sister? Why does that make a difference?

Felipe: Because some kids don't have any, but Leah has a lot, and I have more than one and some other kids have more than one sibling and if you add this together it is going to be more than 24 because we have more than one sibling.

Stacy: There are more of blue than of paper that's yellow.

Teacher: You see more blue cards than yellow cards, that's what Vic said. Why do you think there are all of these cards here from 0 to 9 years old, but there are many fewer from 10 and up and they are not all together?

Bruce: Because 14 is 0 and it doesn't have any.

Felipe: I think it's because people don't have that many siblings at home that are like 10, 11, 12, 13, 14, 15 and up. There are too many up on the lower numbers because I think people at home have more littler siblings than older siblings.

Teacher: Felipe is saying that the reason that these are together is that there are more siblings at home who are younger than us than those who are older than us. How can we check this? How can we be sure?

Felipe: Count the young ones and the old ones.

The class counts 21 siblings aged 0–5.

Teacher: Should we just count siblings older than our group or should we also count the siblings that are our age?

Class: All of them!

The class counts all of the siblings aged 6–22 and finds that there are 20.

Teacher: From here to here [6 to 22], we have 20 siblings. Which has more?

Felipe: Younger.

Teacher: How many more does this group [0 to 5] have than this group [6 to 22]?

Felipe: 1.

While this discussion begins with a very open-ended question of "What do you notice?", students' observations focus on some very specific and important aspects of the data. Grade 1 students are eager to count and compare amounts and figure out which has the most. In this discussion, students point out which ages "have the most" and which ages have the same numbers of people. The teacher records these quantities but also helps keep the focus on what the data tell about the students and their siblings by asking students what numbers stand for. The way the data is displayed encourages students to make comparisons between the siblings and the students in the class. The teacher, through questioning them about their observations, asks the students to think about why the data might be this way.

Student Math Handbook

The *Student Math Handbook* pages related to this unit are pictured on the following pages. Encourage students to use the **Math Words and Ideas** pages as a summary of the math content covered in class. Remind students to think about and answer the question(s) at the bottom of many of these pages. Students can use the **Games** pages to review game directions during class or at home.

When students take the *Student Math Handbook* home, they and their families can discuss these pages together to reinforce or enhance students' understanding of the mathematical concepts and games in this unit.

Calendar

Math Words
• calendar

A calendar is a tool. It shows days and months in a year. A calendar can also show important days and events.

days of the week   month   **September 2009**   year

Sunday	Monday	Tuesday	Wednesday	Thursday	Friday	Saturday
	1	2 First Day of School	3	4	5	
6	7	8 Family Breakfast	9	10	11	12
13	14	15	16	17 Trip to the Park	18	19
20	21	22 First Day of Fall	23	24	25	26
27	28	29	30			

? What happens on Tuesday, September 8?
What day of the week is the first day of school?
When does fall begin?

seventeen **17**

▶ Math Words and Ideas, p. 17

Calendar: Days of the Week

Math Words
• days
• week
• hours

There are 7 days in a week.

Sunday	Monday	Tuesday	Wednesday	Thursday	Friday	Saturday

? What day comes before Wednesday?
What day comes after Friday?

There are 24 hours in a day.

A day is the time between bedtime tonight and bedtime tomorrow.

One day lasts from sunrise to sunrise.

? What day is today? What day is tomorrow?
What day was yesterday?

18 eighteen

▶ Math Words and Ideas, p. 18

Counting by Groups (page 1 of 2)

You can count more quickly if you count by groups. Each time you say a number, you add another group. Every group must have the same number of objects in it.

Each hand has 5 fingers. You can count by 5s to find the total number of fingers. You say every fifth number when you count by 5s.

Counting fingers by 5s

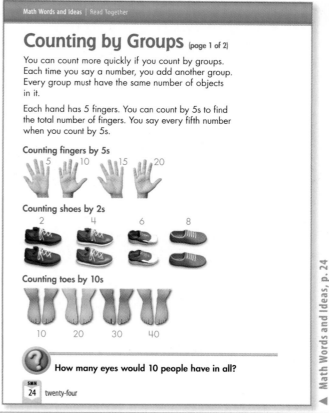

5   10   15   20

Counting shoes by 2s

2   4   6   8

Counting toes by 10s

10   20   30   40

? How many eyes would 10 people have in all?

24 twenty-four

▶ Math Words and Ideas, p. 24

Panel 1 (top left)

Math Words and Ideas | Read Together

Counting by Groups (page 2 of 2)

Here are 23 pennies.

You can count the pennies in different ways.

Counting by 2s

2 4 6 8 10 12 14 16 18 20 22 23

Counting by 5s

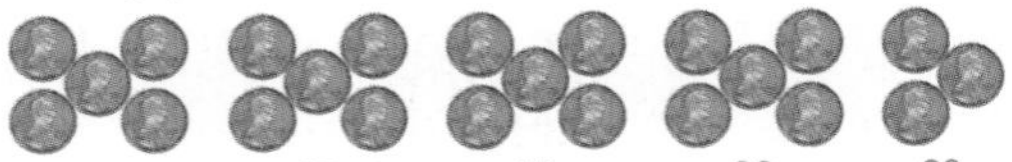

5   10   15   20   23

Counting by 10s

10   20   23

How many different ways can you count 18 pennies?

twenty-five **SMH 25**

▲ Math Words and Ideas, p. 25

Panel 2 (top right)

Math Words and Ideas | Read Together

Number Line

A number line is a tool. It shows numbers in order.

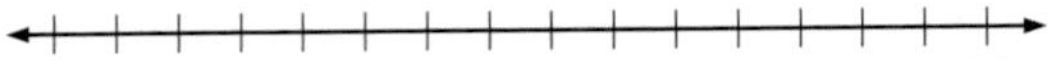

0 1 2 3 4 5 6 7 8 9 10 11 12 13 14 15

You can use it to count forward or back.

When we count forward, the numbers go up.

1, 2, 3, 4, 5, 6.

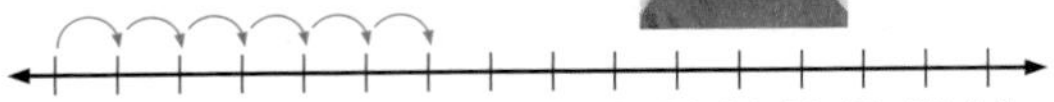

0 1 2 3 4 5 6 7 8 9 10 11 12 13 14 15

When we count back, the numbers go down.

5, 4, 3, 2, 1, 0.

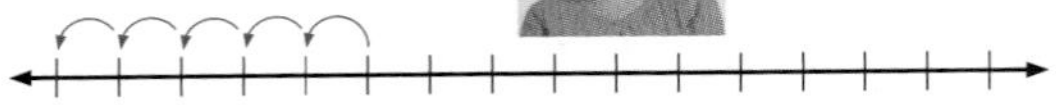

0 1 2 3 4 5 6 7 8 9 10 11 12 13 14 15

Start with 0 and count to 15.
Start with 12 and count to 0.

0 1 2 3 4 5 6 7 8 9 10 11 12 13 14 15

SMH 26 twenty-six

▲ Math Words and Ideas, p. 26

Panel 3 (bottom left)

Math Words and Ideas | Read Together

100 Chart (page 1 of 3)

The 100 chart is a tool that shows numbers from 1 to 100, in order. It can help you count, add, and subtract.

column →

row →

1	2	3	4	5	6	7	8	9	10
11	12	13	14	15	16	17	18	19	20
21	22	23	24	25	26	27	28	29	30
31	32	33	34	35	36	37	38	39	40
41	42	43	44	45	46	47	48	49	50
51	52	53	54	55	56	57	58	59	60
61	62	63	64	65	66	67	68	69	70
71	72	73	74	75	76	77	78	79	80
81	82	83	84	85	86	87	88	89	90
91	92	93	94	95	96	97	98	99	100

How many rows are in the 100 chart?
How many numbers are in each row?
How many columns are in the 100 chart?
How many numbers are in each column?

twenty-seven **SMH 27**

▲ Math Words and Ideas, p. 27

Panel 4 (bottom right)

Math Words and Ideas | Read Together

100 Chart (page 2 of 3)

1	2	3	4	5	6	7	8	9	10
11	12	13	14	15	16	17	18	19	20
21	22	23	24	25	26	27	28	29	30
31	32	33	34	35	36	37	38	39	40
41	42	43	44	45	46	47	48	49	50
51	52	53	54	55	56	57	58	59	60
61	62	63	64	65	66	67	68	69	70
71	72	73	74	75	76	77	78	79	80
81	82	83	84	85	86	87	88	89	90
91	92	93	94	95	96	97	98	99	100

"In each row, the 10s number stays the same and the 1s number goes up by 1."

"In each column, the 10s number goes up by 1 and the 1s number stays the same."

 What patterns do you notice?

 SMH 28 twenty-eight

▲ Math Words and Ideas, p. 28

Panel 1 (top left)

100 Chart (page 3 of 3)

Some of the numbers on this 100 chart are missing.

1	2	3	4	5	6		8		10
	12	13	14	15	16	17	18	19	20
21	22		24	25	26	27	28	29	30
31	32	33	34				38	39	40
41	42	43	44	45	46	47	48	49	50
51		53	54	55	56	57	58	59	60
61	62	63	64	65	66	67			
71	72	73	74	75	76	77	78	79	80
81	82		84	85	86	87	88	89	90
91	92	93	94	95	96		98	99	100

**What numbers are missing?
How do you know?**

twenty-nine · SMH 29

◀ Math Words and Ideas, p. 29

Panel 2 (top right)

Solving Addition Problems (page 1 of 5)

Here is a story problem:

Kim has 3 crayons. Sam gives her 4 more.
How many crayons does Kim have now?

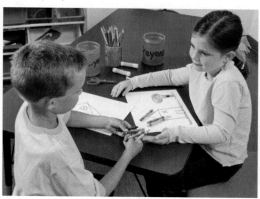

**Does Kim have more crayons at the beginning
or the end of the story?**

thirty-three · SMH 33

◀ Math Words and Ideas, p. 33

Panel 3 (bottom left)

Solving Addition Problems (page 2 of 5)

Here is the story:

Kim has 3 crayons. Sam gives her 4 more.
How many crayons does Kim have now?

There are many ways to solve this problem.
Here is what some children did:

Paula took 3 crayons.
Then she took 4.
Then she counted.

1 2 3   1 2 3 4
1 2 3   4 5 6 7

Pei drew 4 lines.
Then he drew 3 lines.
He counted on from 4.

4   5 6 7

I know that 3 + 3 = 6.
So 3 + 4 is one more.

How would you solve this problem?

SMH 34 · thirty-four

◀ Math Words and Ideas, p. 34

Panel 4 (bottom right)

Solving Addition Problems (page 3 of 5)

Math Words
- equation
- plus
- equal to
- addend
- sum
- equal sign

Kim has 3 crayons. Sam gives her 4 more.
Now Kim has 7 crayons.

Here are 2 equations for this problem.

$$3 + 4 = 7$$

3 plus 4 is equal to 7.

$$7 = 3 + 4$$

7 is equal to 3 plus 4.

3 and 4 are the addends. 7 is the total, or the sum.

The equal sign shows that 3 + 4 is the same amount as 7.

thirty-five · SMH 35

◀ Math Words and Ideas, p. 35

Solving Addition Problems (page 4 of 5)

Here is a story problem:

Rosa has 8 shells.
Sam gives her 3 more shells.
Max gives her 2 more shells.
How many shells does Rosa have now?

 Does Rosa have more shells at the beginning or at the end of the story?

▲ Math Words and Ideas, p. 36

Solving Addition Problems (page 5 of 5)

There are many ways to solve this problem.
This is what some children did:

Paul drew and counted each shell.

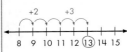

Isabel counted on from 8 on a number line.

8 9 10 11 12 (13) 14 15

Vic used a combination of 10.

8 + 2 = 10

Then he counted on.

11, 12, 13

I know that
2 + 3 = 5.
Then, I count on
6, 7, 8, 9, 10,
11, 12, 13.

How would you solve the problem?

▲ Math Words and Ideas, p. 37

Solving Subtraction Problems (page 1 of 5)

Here is a story problem:

Sam had 10 pennies.
He spent 6 on a pencil.
How many pennies did he have left?

 Does Sam have more pennies at the beginning of the story or at the end?

▲ Math Words and Ideas, p. 38

Solving Subtraction Problems (page 2 of 5)

There are many ways to solve this problem.
This is what some children did.

Kim drew 10 circles and crossed out 6. Then she counted how many were left.

Vic counted back 6 on a number line.

3 (4) 5 6 7 8 9 10

Max counted up from 6 to 10.

7 8 9 10

Then he counted his fingers:
1, 2, 3, 4

Rosa used what she knew about addition combinations.

I know that
4 + 6 = 10.
So, 10 − 6
must be 4.

How would you solve the problem?

▲ Math Words and Ideas, p. 39

Solving Subtraction Problems (page 3 of 5)

Math Words
- minus
- equals
- difference

Sam had 10 pennies.
He spent 6 on a pencil.
Now he has 4.

Here is an equation for this problem.

$$10 - 6 = 4$$

10 minus 6 equals 4

The difference between 10 and 6 is 4.

The equal sign shows that $10 - 6$ is the same amount as 4.

▲ Math Words and Ideas, p. 40

Solving Subtraction Problems (page 4 of 5)

Here is a story problem.

Max had 15 pennies in his piggy bank. He took out 7 pennies to buy a pencil. How many pennies are still in his piggy bank?

 Does Max have more pennies in his bank at the beginning of the story or at the end?

▲ Math Words and Ideas, p. 41

Sorting

Math Words
- sort

You can sort data or objects in different ways. Sorting into groups can show what is the same and what is different about the data or the objects.

Lyle collected buttons.
He wanted to find out what was the same and what was different about the buttons.

First he sorted them by size, like this.

Big Buttons	Medium Buttons	Small Buttons

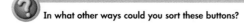

Then he noticed that he could also sort by color.

Red Buttons	Blue Buttons	Orange Buttons

 In what other ways could you sort these buttons?

▲ Math Words and Ideas, p. 64

Data

Math Words
- data

Data means information. You collect data by asking the same question to a group of people.

Marta wanted to get a dog. Her mother told her that first she needed to learn how to take care of a dog. Marta began by collecting data on who she knew who had a dog.

Marta asked this question:

Do you have a dog?

 What are some things you have collected data about?

▲ Math Words and Ideas, p. 65

Math Words and Ideas | Read Together

Surveys

Math Words
• survey

One way to find out what you want to know is to use a survey. A survey is asking a group of people the same question and keeping track of their answers.

Marta's survey

Do you have a dog?

Yes	No
Allie	Bruce
Carol	Teo
Diego	Emilia
Felipe	Leah
Lyle	Paul
Paula	William
Stacy	Libby
	Vic
	Tamika
	Chris
	Nicky
	Isabel
	Toshi

How many classmates did Marta ask?
Who could Marta ask for advice about how to take care of a dog?

SMH
66 sixty-six

▲ Math Words and Ideas, p. 66

Math Words and Ideas | Read Together

Tally Marks

Math Words
• tally mark

Making tally marks is one way to represent data. One tally mark, or line, stands for one answer, or thing, that you are collecting data about. After you make a tally mark for each item, you count them to find the total.

Marta used tally marks to count her data. She made 4 lines. Then she drew a line across the 4 marks to show a group of 5. Here is how Marta counted the answers to her survey question.

Do you have a dog?

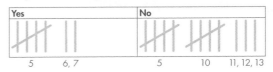

Look at Marta's data.
How many students do not have a dog?
How many students did Marta survey?

sixty-seven SMH **67**

▲ Math Words and Ideas, p. 67

Math Words and Ideas | Read Together

Representation

Math Words
• representation

A representation of data is a way to show other people what you found out.

Here is Marta's representation:

Dogs	No Dogs	
Allie	Bruce	Dear Mom,
Carol	Teo	I collected data about the kids in my class who have dogs. I found out that 7 kids in my class have dogs.
Diego	Emilia	
Felipe	Leah	
Lyle	Paul	
Paula	William	When I need to know how to take care of my dog, there are 7 kids I can ask for advice. Can I get a dog, please?
Stacy	Libby	
	Vic	
	Tamika	
	Chris	Love,
	Nicky	Marta
	Isabel	
	Toshi	

SMH
68 sixty-eight

▲ Math Words and Ideas, p. 68

Math Words and Ideas | Read Together

Sorting Shapes (page 1 of 2)

Look at this group of shapes.
How are these shapes the same? How are they different?
Think about different ways you could sort them into groups.

Max sorted these shapes like this.

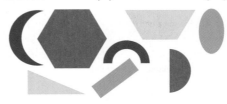

Shapes with curves | Shapes with only straight sides

What is another way to sort these shapes?

SMH
76 seventy-six

▲ Math Words and Ideas, p. 76

Sorting Shapes (page 2 of 2)

Here's another group of shapes.

Rosa sorted these shapes like this.

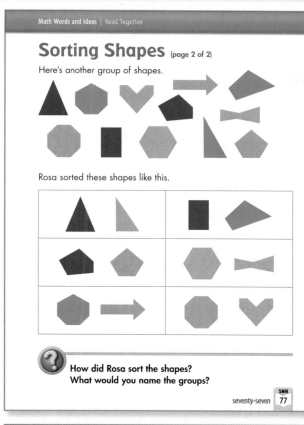

**How did Rosa sort the shapes?
What would you name the groups?**

seventy-seven **SMH 77**

Math Words and Ideas, p. 77

Guess My Rule (page 1 of 2)

When you play *Guess My Rule* with shapes, one player picks some shapes that fits a secret rule.

The shapes inside the circle fit Sam's rule.
The shapes outside the circle do not fit Sam's rule.

Can you guess Sam's rule?

SMH 78 seventy-eight

Math Words and Ideas, p. 78

Guess My Rule (page 2 of 2)

The shapes inside this circle fit Kim's rule.
The shapes outside the circle do not fit Kim's rule.

Can you guess Kim's rule?

seventy-nine **SMH 79**

Math Words and Ideas, p. 79

Games | Read Together

Guess My Rule

You need

- 20–25 buttons
- sorting mats

Play with a group of 2–4 players.

1. Player 1 chooses a rule that fits some of the buttons and writes it on a piece of paper.

2. Player 1 puts two buttons that fit the rule on the "These Fit My Rule" paper and two buttons that don't fit the rule on the "These Don't Fit My Rule" paper.

3. Player 2 puts a button where he or she thinks it belongs.

4. Players take turns placing buttons.

5. After each player has placed 3 buttons, players may try to guess the rule on their next turn.

6. The game is over once the rule has been guessed correctly.

7. Play again. Another player chooses the rule.

SMH
G12

▲ Games, G12

Index